Free!

A PLAY BY DAVID GRANT

www.heinemann.co.uk

✓ Free online support
✓ Useful weblinks
✓ 24 hour online ordering

01865 888080

Heinemann

Heinemann is an imprint of Pearson Education Limited, a company incorporated in England and Wales, having its registered office at Edinburgh Gate, Harlow, Essex, CM20 2JE. Registered company number: 872828

www.heinemann.co.uk

Heinemann is a registered trademark of Pearson Education Limited

Text © Heinemann 2008

First published 2008

17
13

British Library Cataloguing in Publication Data
A catalogue record for this book is available from the British Library

ISBN 978 0 435233 46 4

Typeset by Phoenix Photosetting, Chatham, Kent, UK
Printed in China (CTPS/13)

Contents

Teaching resources

To help deliver the questions and activities on pages 83–93, teaching materials are available to download free from www.heinemann.co.uk/literature

---

Websites

There are links to relevant websites in this book and in the online material. In order to ensure that the links are up to date, that the links work, and that the sites are not inadvertantly linked to sites that could be considered offensive, we have made the links available on the Heinemann website at www.heinemann.co.uk/hotlinks. When you access the site, the express code is 3464.

Introduction

Free Lesson is a play aimed directly at the Key Stage Three classroom. It is a school drama, set in a classroom, with 23 speaking parts, all of them school students. It is a play about the people who will perform and study it.

Although each act is divided into scenes, there should be no pause between them. The cast forms groups either standing or sitting around the set; these rotate as the audience's focus shifts from scene to scene.

It is based on a simple premise: a class should have a supply teacher for their first lesson of the day but the supply teacher does not turn up. The class agree among themselves that they will not report the incident but try to get through the lesson unsupervised and undetected.

With a constantly revolving focus around the classroom – the students, their observations and concerns – the dramatic thrust of the play moves through three phases:

- the realisation that they have been left unsupervised and the argument about whether to report the absence
- an expedition to relieve the boredom of their enforced imprisonment in the classroom, in which two of the least likely students are sent to steal the Head teacher's biscuit tin
- a parallel case of theft within the classroom.

It is this last incident which, in the investigation and successful resolution of the crime, pulls the students together in a spirit of adult-less self-regulation.

The play explores and embraces the comprehensive ethos of school and of life, without sacrificing the reality of school and student life to a glib resolution of moral issues. Conflicts of gender, academic ability, and conformism build to the conclusion that – whatever schools and teachers may hope, struggle and aim for – it is the students who decide their own fate, and it is their underlying humanity that sees them through.

Cast list

Liam, *a 'difficult' student*

Nigel, *a disorganised boy*

Tom, *sometimes known as Snotty Tom, a good boy*

Robbie, *a keen and able student, friends with Tom and Andrew*

Gemma, *an outspoken girl*

Alison, *a quiet, organised girl*

Stuart, *Liam's friend and 'partner-in-crime'*

Darren, *an optimist, Nigel's friend*

Andrew, *a good boy, Tom's friend*

Lisa, *Gemma's willing shadow, following her everywhere*

Briony and Roni, *quiet girls, Alison's friends*

Neil, *a pessimist*

Craig, *a sportsman*

Ben, *an outsider in the group*

Dan, *a boy with a sense of humour*

Kayleigh, *a girl with attitude*

Katie and Hattie, *two friends*

Laura B, Laura E, Daisy and Sara, *friends who constantly fall in and out with each other*

Act One

Scene 1

A classroom with desks/tables in rows. Within the classroom there is a display board showing students' work, a large metal storage cupboard, a teacher's desk – unoccupied – and a door into the corridor. The students are sitting or lolling on desks, or standing around talking. Although none are shouting, their combined noise is impressive.

Sudden silence.

All the students sink or slide slowly, almost imperceptibly, into their seats. Liam sits in the very middle of the room. Alison and Craig on the front row. All eyes, in unison, follow the (invisible to the audience) teacher to his desk – except one.

Liam, a fashionably scruffy, just the right side of grubby, boy lolls on his desk chatting away to Darren who tries to listen without appearing to. Meanwhile, the others answer the (inaudible to the audience) register in still and frightened silence.

LAURA B   Yes, Mr Lewis.

BEN   Yes, sir.

DARREN   Sir.

BRIONY   Yes, sir.

RONI   Yes, sir.   5

LIAM   *(excitedly to Darren)* You haven't? I can't believe it! You haven't played it yet? Oh *(pause)* my *(pause)* God!

SARA	*(wearily correcting Mr Lewis' repeated mispronunciation)* Sara, sir ... Not Sarah, sir. *(pause)* Yes, sir. 10
DAN	Rhymes with tiara, sir. *(pause)* Wasn't meant to be funny, sir. *(sulking playfully)* Just trying to be helpful, sir.
LIAM	So you're climbing down, yeah *(miming actions)* and they're shooting at you, yeah? 15 And you jump – weeeeeee –
DAISY	Yes, Mr Lewis.
LAURA E	Yes, sir.
LIAM	And, then, like, kabboooooom!
NEIL	Here, sir. 20
LIAM	And he goes *(robotic, monotone voice)* 'Stop or we must eliminate you, intruder'.
STUART	Yes, Mr Lewis.
LIAM	Or something like that, anyway.
HATTIE	Yes, Mr Lewis. 25
LIAM	And you're running and running, right, and they're shooting and you're running ...
CRAIG	Yes, sir.
LIAM	And you're like: bang ... bang ... bang ... bang-bang-bang-BANG! 30
DAN	Good morning, Mr Lewis, sir. *(pauses for Mr Lewis' reply)* And how are you today, sir? *(pauses for reply then subdued as though told off)* Yes, sir, I'm here today, sir.
KATIE	Yes, sir.
LIAM	... big grenade things which just blow them to PIECES! 35

NIGEL   Yes, Mr Lewis.

LIAM   … and they're like *(imitating machine-gun fire)* huh-huh-huh-huh-huh-huh …

GEMMA   Yes, sir.   40

LISA   Yes, Mr Lewis.

Long pause. Everyone turns to Liam.

LIAM   *(knowing he's in trouble, as if finishing his conversation with Darren)* And that's how you get the square root of a prime number. *(pause. As though surprised to be interrupted)* Sir? *(shocked)* Me, sir? I wasn't talking, sir. *(shakes head, explaining his failure to answer the register)* I didn't hear you, sir. Been   45 having ear trouble, sir. *(sticks finger in ear and wiggles, examines finger)* Nasty lot of earwax in there, sir. *(pause)* I don't know how it got there, sir. I didn't put it there.

Laughter from the class. The register resumes.

TOM   Yes, sir. *(sniffs loudly)*   50

ALISON   Yes, sir.

LIAM   *(interrupting)* Oh, so bored …

ANDREW   Yes, Mr Lewis.

ROBBIE   Sir.

LIAM   Why do we have to do this every day?   55 *So* boring …

KAYLEIGH   *(carelessly)* Yeah. *(pause for telling off, then a very deliberate)* Yes … *(pause, adding reluctantly)* … sir.

LIAM   *(hand shoots up)* Sir? Can I go to the loo, sir?   60
        *(already out of his seat on the way to the door, he
        does not wait for an answer)* I'm busting, sir.
        *(from the doorway, replying to the obvious
        suggestion)* I didn't need to go then, sir.
        (loudly from just offstage) I really need a POO!
        (exits)

        *Sniggering and whispering subsides and the class
        settles again. Their heads drop: they are clearly
        being told off.*

        A bell rings.

ALISON *(looking up)* No, sir, it's Monday. We stay in
        here for our lesson. You've got Year 8, sir.   65
        In S6, sir. We've got English with Miss
        Barraclough, sir. In here, sir.

        *All eyes lift, watching the teacher stand, then
        follow him to the door. As he leaves, all visibly
        relax. Some happy, relaxed sighs.*

Scene 2

*Chatter begins, grows in volume as background
noise.*

*Craig and Alison are sharing a desk. Craig –
daringly – stands up, then sits on the desk behind,
his feet on his chair. He scouts around the room –
then notices Alison beside him. She is neatly
unpacking her school bag. She removes – and
places neatly in an orderly sequence on the desk –
a pair of gleaming white trainers, a neatly folded
PE kit, a packed lunch, a drinks flask, a pencil*

case, a homework diary/planner, a dictionary, an exercise book, and a reading book. Throughout, Craig stares open-mouthed, his astonishment growing.

Alison packs the PE and lunch items away leaving an organised desk. She opens her pencil case, removes two pens, a ruler, and a pencil and lines them up on the desk. Craig's open mouth has become a smile, growing broader and broader. He looks around to get others' attention. Gemma sees. He beckons. Gemma comes over. Lisa inevitably follows, hanging on Gemma's every movement and word. Alison, unaware of them, opens her English exercise book, carefully and deliberately places herself in writing position, writes the date and, with a different pen, underlines it.

CRAIG What on *earth* are you doing, Alison?

ALISON *(tentatively)* I'm sorry? Pardon?

CRAIG Have you become mental? Are you a mentalist? What are you *doing*? The teacher's not even here yet and you're writing the date? And underlining it in *gold*?   5

ALISON I like my work to look …

CRAIG *(rummaging in her pencil case)* Gold … Silver … What's this one?

ALISON *(apologetically)* Metallic turquoise.   10

CRAIG And this one?

ALISON *(even more apologetically)* Melon yellow. It smells of … melon.

CRAIG	And what's this? *(picking up her dictionary)*
GEMMA	*(feigning surprise)* Don't you know, Craig? 15 Haven't you seen one before? It's a book.
CRAIG	Of course I—
GEMMA	But it's not any old book. *(pinching his cheek like an auntie)* It's not a story book like the ones we used to read in little school, Craig. 20
CRAIG	I know, but—
GEMMA	It's a *special* book, Craig.
CRAIG	Yeah, but, Gemma—
GEMMA	It tells you what words mean.
CRAIG	But, Gemma— 25
GEMMA	If you don't know a word, you look it up in here and it tells you all about it.
CRAIG	But, Gemma—
GEMMA	All about all the words you've never heard of and never will hear of, Craig. Because you 30 spend all your time running up and down and round and round a field trying to kick a little ball into a big net.
CRAIG	Why don't you—
GEMMA	A little … *(she taps him on the head)* … 35 round … *(tap tap)* … ball … *(tap)* … full of nothing … *(tap)* … but air … *(tap)* … like your head *(slap)*.
LISA	Yeah, your head.
GEMMA	Shut up, Lisa. 40

Gemma wanders off. Lisa follows. Craig sags, briefly deflated before wandering off to a safer part of the classroom.

Scene 3

GEMMA   Teacher's not coming. Miss Barraclough's ill.
Nasty cough. She smokes, you know.

LISA   *(looking on in amazed admiration)* How do you
know all this, Gemma?

GEMMA   Keep my eyes open. Ear to the ground, Lisa.   5
Live opposite her house. If you want to know
about a teacher, Lisa, that's my advice. Move
into the house opposite them. My mum saw
her this morning. Lives with her boyfriend,
Miss Barraclough does. Could be her dad   10
but I don't think so. Been together three
years now. He's something big in computers.
He's something big wherever he is. About
twenty stone, I reckon. The pavement creaks
when he comes out the house. Needs two   15
seats on the bus. Don't blame her for not
marrying him. I wouldn't marry him. I might
run round him for the exercise but I
wouldn't marry him.

LISA   *(to Laura B)* Teacher's not coming. Got a   20
cough. She—

NEIL   *(grumpily to no one in particular)* 'Course
they're coming. They always send
someone.

LAURA B   *(to Sara)* Teacher's not coming, Sara.   25

SARA   *(to Daisy)* Teacher's not coming, Daisy.

DAISY   *(to Laura E)* Teacher's not coming, Laura.

*Word spreads. Lots of quiet cheering and
punching of the air.*

LIAM *(offstage, throwing open classroom door and speaking in a deep, gruff teacher voice)* Will you PLEASE sit down and be quiet.

Darren, and others, jump – and hurriedly begin to settle in their seats until they see who it is.

LIAM *(grinning)* It's me! Did I get you? Eh? Eh? 30

DARREN Yeah, I was really scared, Liam.

LIAM You were, weren't you? Eh? Eh? I saw you jump! Oi, Stuart! Stuart, did you see Darren jump when I did the teacher thing? Did you see him? He was like … *(mimics Darren* 35 *jumping out of his skin)*

Nigel moves to the classroom door on lookout.

STUART Oi! Briony! And Briony's friend! Keep the noise down! *(Briony and Roni smile weakly, look embarrassed and continue their inaudible, shy whispering)* Teacher's not coming, Liam.

LIAM *(punching the air)* Yessssssss! 40

GEMMA *(over her shoulder to Liam)* She's in hospital. Got trampled by an elephant, escaped from the zoo. Big footprint, right in the middle of her face. *(on her way past Tom and Andrew, who are sitting quietly on the front row)* Isn't that 45 right, Snotty Tom?

Scene 4

TOM *(snorting and sniffing as always)* Don't call me that! Why do they always call me that? *(sniff)* I can't help it! I've seen doctors! In London!

ANDREW Forget it, mate. Just leave it. We've just got to wait for the teacher to come. 5

TOM *(sniff)* The teacher's not coming, Andrew. You heard them.

ANDREW Someone'll come. A supply teacher. They're always late.

TOM *(sniff)* It's been five minutes. Nearly six. 10 *(snort)* Maybe we should go to the office and tell them. *(sniff)* Tell them to send a supply teacher.

ALISON *(leaning over)* I don't mind going to the office. Shall I? 15

ROBBIE *(leaning forward)* I think we can risk a few more minutes. The more … aggressive members of the class may be unhappy with anyone who encourages the office to send a teacher. *(to Briony, beside him)* Do *you* want 20 to go and get a teacher, Briony?

Briony and Roni look terrified; they shake their heads quickly and firmly.

BRIONY *(timidly)* Perhaps we should just wait and see if someone comes? *(she continues to speak inaudibly to Roni)*

Nigel, still at the door, freezes.

NIGEL *(loud whisper)* Teacher!

Everyone races to their desks and sits – except Liam who makes a point of sauntering casually to his place. Nigel remains on guard, ready to sprint. Pause.

NIGEL	False alarm. *(Liam instantly turns on his heels like a figure skater and returns to his original position)* He's gone past. That PE bloke.	
DARREN	The one with the hair? Mr Barrington?	25
ROBBIE	Bonnington.	
DARREN	Bonnington. He's always late for his lesson. Always eating. Sausage rolls, usually. Ketchup all down his tracksuit.	
NIGEL	He's coming back! *(everyone dashes to their seats again – except Liam who stays put. All eyes trained on the door for ten long seconds)*	30
LIAM	*(dismissively)* He's lost or he's forgotten something, he's not coming in here.	
NIGEL	He's gone past again.	
LIAM	Told you.	

Scene 5

ROBBIE	*(loud enough for the whole class to hear)* Perhaps we *should* go the office and tell them? They'll realise sooner or later that the teacher hasn't—	
LIAM	*(approaching rapidly)* Oh, shut up, Robbie, you boffin!	5
ROBBIE	If we don't tell anyone, we'll get in trouble. They'll say we should have told the office. I'd rather sit here with a supply teacher for an hour – in fact there are only fifty two minutes remaining of the lesson – than spend break in here, or lunchtime, because we sat and took no action when we should have done.	10

LIAM	*(mimicking him)* Took no action? Took no action? 15

> *Sensing and hoping for trouble, Craig and Stuart arrive beside Liam.*

STUART Oi! Briony! And Briony's friend! I told you before! Keep the noise down or they'll realise we haven't got a teacher! *(laughs and elbows Craig, encouraging him to join in. Again, Briony and Roni smile weakly, and look embarrassed)*

NEIL *(grumpily to no one in particular)* We're going to end up staying in all break. And lunchtime, 20 too, most probably …

GEMMA Got plans have you, Neil? Got a table booked in the canteen? Table for two? Taking her out clubbing afterwards, are you? Chess club? In the library? *(Neil's perpetual scowl continues)* 25

ROBBIE If they find out we sat here for an hour without a teacher, they'll take an hour away from us – or more: breaks, lunchtimes, an hour after school … They won't let us have a free lesson for nothing. 30

STUART Oh shut up you boffin!

LIAM Yeah, shut up you *thick* boffin! Don't you understand? *(he explains slowly, word by word)* If we don't tell them the teacher never arrived, they might not find out. 35

ROBBIE And then again they might. And I'd rather be a thick boffin than just thick … *(Liam grabs him)* And I'd rather sit here for … *(struggles to check his watch)* forty nine minutes listening

to a teacher than wondering who you're   40
going to thump next.

The struggle continues. Slowly, Briony, sitting beside Robbie, is getting squashed.

LIAM   No need to wonder. It's going to be you I'm thumping every time, if you go and get a teacher.

BRIONY   *(emerging from beneath the struggling boys, angry but with great dignity)* Can you *please*   45
stop it?! I'm sitting here quietly, minding my own business, chatting to my friend – whose name is Roni, by the way, as you hadn't taken the trouble to ask – and you two boys can't even sit in a classroom for ten minutes   50
without starting a fight and, and, *squashing* me.

The class have fallen silent, staring in amazement – this is the most Briony has ever spoken. She struggles to continue – but does, now everyone is looking.

BRIONY   And … and … it's pathetic. The teachers can't even leave us alone for ten minutes! *(gaining in confidence, almost shouting)* Can't   55
you even behave like … like decent human beings unless there's a teacher in the room? We haven't got anyone to tell us what to do, how to behave … but just because we don't *have* to behave like human beings, doesn't   60
mean we *can't*.

Ten seconds of stunned silence, then whispering grows into muttering.

Scene 6

GEMMA   No, she's right. Listen to me … How long have
         we been here? How long have we been waiting
         for a teacher to come? Ten minutes? Fifteen?

ROBBIE   Thirteen.

GEMMA   Thank you, Professor Robbie. Thirteen   5
         minutes we've been sitting here, patiently
         waiting for a responsible adult. Someone to
         improve our learning, to feed our growing
         minds, to make us better and more beautiful
         people. And no one's shown up. If they   10
         knew we were sitting here on our own, if
         they knew we didn't have a teacher, they
         would have sent a supply teacher by now. So
         obviously they don't know we haven't got a
         teacher. And no one's coming.   15

LIAM AND STUART   Yesssssss!

LISA   That's right.

GEMMA   So either we go and tell the office – and end
         up copying out of a book for three quarters
         of an hour – or we deal with it ourselves. If   20
         we fight, if we do something stupid, if we
         don't work together, we'll get caught. But if
         we can look after ourselves: no detention at
         break, no lunchtime, no after school.
         Freedom, my people, freedom!   25

         *Most of the class exchange grins. They have been
         won over.*

LIAM   What's the point of not having a teacher if
         we don't do anything stupid?

NEIL *(grumpily, to himself)* There'll be a teacher here in five minutes. An angry one. Betcha.

Scene 7

ALISON It's not fair if we all have to stay in because they won't go and get a teacher.

ANDREW No, I think Gemma's right. We might just get away with it – if we're sensible.

TOM Yeah, but that's a big 'if' for some of   5
them ... *(sniff)* ... us.

ROBBIE What's the point of coming to school if we're just going to sit here and do nothing? I can stay at home and do that – clutch my stomach, tell my mum I'm ill. And I don't   10
have to get up at 7 o'clock and put on this stupid uniform and walk half-way across town to do it, either: just lie in bed groaning a bit. If I'm here, there should be a teacher here, doing what they're supposed to be   15
doing. And if there isn't, we should go and get one. The trouble with that lot *(indicates Gemma, Liam, etc.)* is they don't think about other people.

ANDREW I'd rather be doing nothing than copying   20
out, Robbie – that's what supply teachers always give you. It's only one lesson we're missing. The teacher'll turn up for the next lesson. We couldn't get this lucky two lessons running ... I say we sit here and do nothing.   25

TOM *(sniff)* You're just scared Liam'll kill you if you go and get a teacher, Andrew.

ANDREW Yup.

Scene 8

LIAM OK. So you've got Bonnington.

DARREN Who?

LIAM The PE teacher.

DARREN The one with the hair? Barrington?

LIAM Bonnington! And you've got that other PE   5
bloke … whatsisname … Kendrick … in a
fight. Who wins?

STUART Kendrick. Obviously. Bonnington's got a
sandwich in one hand and a cake in the
other, his belly's dragging along the floor,   10
how's he going to hit anyone?

DAN He could sit on Kendrick. Drop his belly on
him. Suffocate him.

NIGEL Why are they having a fight, anyway?   15

LIAM 'Cos Bonnington's borrowed Kendrick's trackie
bots without asking … They're not having a
fight, you idiot! It's just an imaginary … thing.

DAN OK. You've got Smallwood and—

DARREN Who? Who's Smallwood?   20

DAN The geography teacher. Your geography
teacher, Darren. For the last two years.

DARREN Right.

STUART Smallwood? He's about seventy. He'd blow
away in a breeze. He'd fall over if you   25
breathed too hard on him.

LIAM A lot of people fall over when *you* breathe on
them, Stuart. Dog-breath.

DAN So you've got Smallwood – the Pensioner
Punisher – and you've got Dexter.   30

DARREN	Who's Dex—

DAN Oh, for God's sake, Darren, how long have you been at this school? He's the maths teacher. You know *(impersonating him, building up to a deafening crescendo)* You are 35
trying my patience, BOY! You are ab-so-lutely IM *(pause)* POSSIBLE!

DARREN Oh, him.

DAN *(tiring slightly)* So, you've got Smallwood and Dexter in a fight. Who wins? 40

DARREN Which one's Smallwood again?

Groans all round.

Scene 9

LAURA B So let me get this straight, Daisy. Sara's going on holiday with you to your dad's. In Wales.

DAISY Cornwall.

LAURA B Wales, Cornwall, wherever, that's not the point. And Laura's going on holiday with 5
you to your dad's. In *Cornwall. (Daisy nods)*
In fact, everyone's going on holiday with you to your dad's. In Cornwall. Except me.

SARA There isn't room for all of us. Daisy's dad says.

LAURA B Oh, you've been on the phone to him, have 10
you? Rings up for a chat most weekends, does he, Sara?

LAURA E Daisy's said she's sorry!

DAISY And you can definitely come next time.

LAURA B Next time?! Next time?! I'd rather stick 15

broken glass in my eyes … *(folds arms and turns away)*

Scene 10

LIAM No! No! No! Are you mental, Darren? Are you a mentalist, Darren? There is no way – repeat *no* way – that Mrs Marsh would beat Miss Vernon at arm wrestling. Vernon does metalwork! She bends iron bars with her 5 bare hands. She's got biceps like a truck driver's thighs.

DARREN I'm telling you. Mrs Marsh could take her. Easily. I saw her in Learning Support the other day, moving a filing cabinet. Single- 10 handed. She was all over it.

Pause.

LIAM *(looks around, sighs)* I'm bored now. Let's do something stupid.

Scene 11

Meanwhile on the other side of the room …

GEMMA *(to herself)* I'm bored. We should do something. Something … *good*. We should do something.

LISA Yeah. We should.

KAYLEIGH Like what? 5

GEMMA *(suddenly deflated)* Dunno.

KAYLEIGH What's the point, Gemma? Let's just sit here and get bored like normal.

GEMMA	*(gradually gaining the attention of almost all the rest of the class – except Hattie and Katie who are talking loudly to Laura B in the far corner of the room)* We're sitting here, just waiting to get caught. 10
HATTIE	*(at great speed)* Oh! Oh! I never told you, Laura. You know Maddie was going out with Ryan—
LAURA B	Yeah!
KATIE	—but Ryan really fancied Kelly— 15
LAURA B	No!
HATTIE	—and Kelly was going out with Chris—
GEMMA	Even if we do get caught, so what? A lunchtime? An after-school? Does it matter? Let's do something we'll remember, 20 something that was worth getting caught for … something good … not just stupid kid stuff. Oh, we can sit here and bicker and bitch and fight and chat like we do all the time, but we're on our own. We should … 25 achieve something. We should do something good.
LIAM	What like a sponsored silence? *(goody-goody voice)* One day when the teacher didn't turn up, we raised six pounds forty three for 30 good causes …
GEMMA	Oh, shuttup. I want to do something I can … *(thinks)* … tell the grandchildren about. And what have I got so far? There I'll be, in my big grandma rocking chair, in my curlers, 35 with my blue rinse in a bun, and little Johnny climbs on my knee and says, 'What was it

like at school when you were young,
Grandma?' And I say: 'Well, once, the teacher
didn't turn up and we sat around, and we   40
chatted a bit.' I need something better than
that.

KATIE   —so Chris has a go at Ryan—

HATTIE   —and Kelly chucks him—

LAURA B   No!   45

KATIE   —so she says if you want to go out with me
then fine—

HATTIE   —so he says fine and she does!

GEMMA   Come on! How often does this happen? How
often do we get to do what we want in a   50
lesson?

LIAM   Most days.

GEMMA   I mean the rest of us, Liam, not just you. *(to
everyone)* We should make the most of it.
Grab the opportunity.   55

LISA   Yeah!

KATIE   —but Kelly fancies Lee—

HATTIE   —so Lee goes to Shelley he wants to split up—

KATIE   —and Shelley has a go at Kelly and her
brother gets all gobby—   60

HATTIE   —and goes round her house and her mum
says 'Get out'—

LAURA B   No!

KATIE   —and he says no and she says—   65

GEMMA   *(very loudly)* Will you lot be quiet?! I'm trying
to do something here.

Silence falls.

LISA   *(pointlessly)* Yeah, quiet everyone.

GEMMA   *(calmer)* Have you ever seen *The Great Escape*?

ROBBIE   Are you saying we should dig a tunnel   70
under the school walls and then leg it? I
think we might get in quite a lot of trouble
for that. Also, we might need a spade.

GEMMA   No, Professor Robbie, I'm just saying that in
The Great Escape they didn't hang around   75
shouting about Ryan and Kelly and what her
mum said when he blah blah blah. They *did*
something.

ROBBIE   Didn't they get caught? Or killed?

GEMMA   *(ignoring him)* I wanna get caught for doing   80
something … *big*. So we can walk out of here
with dignity, with respect, with our heads
held high. What we need is a mission. A
challenge.

LIAM   Yesssssss! Like what?   85

Silence.

ANDREW   I know how to hack into the computer
network …

TOM   No, you don't, Andrew. You *think* you do.

LIAM   And we can email dirty pictures to teachers?
Yesssssss!   90

STUART   Yesssssss!

GEMMA   How are you going to get into a computer
room? They're all locked. Or they've got
lessons in them.

ANDREW   *(quietly to Tom)* We're just going to get   95
ourselves in more trouble.

NIGEL	We could nick the caretaker's trolleys and have races.
NEIL	Yeah, they'll never notice us, piling up and down the corridors on two large trolleys. 100 We'll do it really quietly. On tip-toe.
HATTIE	We could give each other makeovers!
GEMMA	*(sarcastically)* Oh, fantastic! Brilliant! We had this lesson once when the teacher didn't turn up. It was rubbish boring – but darling, 105 you should have seen my eye-shadow, it was absolutely divine …
HATTIE	Alright, alright.
DAISY	What about truth-dare? Spin the bottle? We played that at my party. 110
LAURA B	What party? *(Daisy looks embarrassed)*
GEMMA	We can do that anytime. Anywhere. Don't you understand? Don't you see why this is so special? They think we've got a teacher. They think we are being supervised, that we're 115 under control. So they're not worried about us. So we're free. We can go anywhere, do anything—
LIAM	Let's break stuff!
GEMMA	—and as long as it's something a teacher 120 might tell us to do, we won't get done for it! I bet we could … all put our PE kit on, run around the school and no one would say a word.
DAN	Shall we, then? 125
LISA	I haven't got my kit …

GEMMA No, why would we *want* to do that? It's just
an example …

LIAM So what do you wanna do, then?

Pause while they think.

DAN You know that old lady in the office? The   130
grumpy one. Whatsername?

NEIL Mrs Dixon? She's horrible.

KATIE When I broke my arm in netball, she made
me take off my make-up before she'd even
talk to me. I walk in there with my arm   135
hanging off and she gives me a bottle of
make-up remover.

STUART She rang up my mum to tell her I'd been late
for school every day for a fortnight and I
might walk faster if I wasn't so fat.   140

GEMMA When I went to the office with toothache,
she hit me with a stick until I stopped
moving. So she's nasty. What about her?

DAN She's got a tin of biscuits. A big tin.

Silence. Mystified glances exchanged.

LIAM *(sarcastically)* Ooh, she's *lucky*!   145

DAN But they're not *just* biscuits. I've seen her.
Every day at 11 o'clock, she gets out a plate
(miming the actions) … and a little doily …
and she gets the tin out of the cupboard
behind her desk … and she opens it …   150
and she puts a little bourbon on the plate …
and a little custard cream … and a little pink
wafer … and she takes it into the Head with

his morning coffee. They're not *just* biscuits
… they're *Head teacher* biscuits. *(pause for* 155
dramatic effect) We should nick them. And eat
them. Now that *would* be a challenge.

Pause for the class' consideration.

LISA *(hopefully)* Are there any … chocolate biscuits?

DAN Hundreds of them.

*General noises of agreement to the plan from
everyone except Katie, Hattie and Stuart.*

KATIE But she sits at that desk all day.   160

DAN And that's the challenge!

HATTIE And if she catches you, she'll peel you, cook
you, and eat you alive.

GEMMA And that's the challenge!

STUART But it's just stupid. Pointless.   165

DAN That's the whole point … stupid.

GEMMA Whoa, whoa, whoa! There's nothing stupid
about biscuits.

BEN If you want to do something serious, we
could start a fire.   170

Silence. Nervous glances from everyone.

ALISON *(aside)* Is he joking?

ROBBIE *(aside)* You just can't tell with Ben, can you?

Scene 12

DAN So, the biscuits it is, then. Next question: who?

LIAM What do you mean, who?

DAN	Who's going to go and nick the biscuits?

Pause. Some eyes look round the room; some look firmly down.

LIAM	Snotty Tom!	
TOM	Shut up, Liam …	5
STUART	It was your idea, Gemma.	
GEMMA	Nicking the biscuits was Dan's idea.	
DAN	We should draw straws for it.	
CRAIG	And it should be two people. A boy and a girl.	
TOM	*(sniff)* I don't wanna do it.	10
KATIE	No, me neither.	
KAYLEIGH	I'm not doing it. I'm not. And that's final.	
LIAM	I'll do it! I don't care. Doesn't bother me.	
STUART	Yeah, come on, it'll be a laugh.	
LIAM	Yeah, we'll do it.	15
GEMMA	No, we should draw straws.	
LIAM	*(angrily)* Why?	
GEMMA	Because we're all doing this. We're all going to get in trouble if we get caught. This isn't you just doing your usual 'The Liam Show'. This is all of us.	20

Pause while Liam takes this in and develops a sulk.

GEMMA	Right, Alison, tear a couple of pages out the middle of your English book and then tear it into strips. OK? We'll need … *(counts heads)* … ten for the boys and eleven for the girls, plus one extra. OK?	25

ALISON *(quietly horrified)* Tear pages? Out of my
English book?

ROBBIE Don't worry, I'll get them out of mine, you
won't need to trash your beloved book.   30
(he starts tearing)

GEMMA Right, Dan, you can hold the girls' straws;
Lisa, you can hold the boys'.

LISA *(genuinely surprised and delighted)* Really?
Thanks, Gemma!

GEMMA OK, boys, you come and collect a straw one   35
at a time from Lisa. Girls, you do the same
from Dan. Straws ready? *(she takes the straws
and tears one in half)* Right. There are two
short ones. One for the boys *(gives it to Lisa)*
and one for the girls *(gives it to Dan, then*   40
*distributes the longer straws between Lisa and
Dan. They clutch them in their fists, the ends
poking out the top)* Whoever gets the short
straws is going on a mission. OK? Everyone
come and take a straw.

No one moves.

GEMMA I'll go first then, shall I? *(tentatively takes a
straw – it's a long one)*
Who's next?   45

Still no one moves. Nervous laughter.

GEMMA Dan, Lisa, you take yours.

*Lisa watches nervously as Dan goes first. He pulls
it out of Lisa's fist very slowly. Tension mounts.
It's not the short one. Lisa's go. She grabs one,*

pulling it out at speed. It's not the short one. She is clearly highly relieved.

GEMMA 'Course, the longer you leave it, the more straws get taken, the more chance you've got of getting the short straw.

ROBBIE Actually, that's not strictly true because— 50

GEMMA Shut it, professor. Take a straw.

Robbie does. It's a long straw. Gradually, reluctantly, the others are shuffling forwards. They end up in a queue of three or four, the girls queuing towards Dan, the boys towards Lisa. As each leaves the queue highly relieved, others join.

BEN I'll go next. I hate waiting for stuff. Buses … Laura B to fall in love with me … *(he grins leerily at her)* … old age … death.

LAURA B He's getting weirder. He's *scary*. 55

Laura B picks a long straw.

SARA I'm telling you, if it's Ben who gets it, I'm not going. I'm not going with him, I'm telling you. He is SOOOOO weeeeeeird.

Ben picks a long straw.

DAISY *(smiling)* What about Craig? Would you go with him? 60

SARA Shuttup, Daisy!

Sara picks a long straw.

LAURA E I'd go with Craig!

DAISY You'd go with anyone who asked.

Daisy picks a long straw.

LAURA E Shut UP, Daisy!

CRAIG *(giving his most charming smile)* Ready when 65
you are, Laura.

LAURA E SHUT UP, Craig.

Craig picks a long straw.

DARREN *(a quiet prayer to himself)* Please, please,
please, please, please, please …

Laura E picks a long straw.

NEIL Don't worry, it'll be me that gets it. I'm 70
telling you …

Darren picks a long straw.

GEMMA Oi! Liam, Stuart, come on. Come and pick.

LIAM Us? Little old us? No, we'll let everybody else
do it. We wouldn't want it to be just another
episode of 'The Liam Show', would we? 75

STUART 'The Liam and Stuart Show'.

LIAM No, it's just called 'The Liam Show'. You're
not in it.

Neil picks a long straw.

NEIL *(grumpily)* I told you it wouldn't be me. It
never is … 80

ANDREW Why am I doing this? It's just peer pressure. I
don't even like biscuits all that much …

*Tom picks. It's the short straw. It's him. In the
girls' queue Katie, about to pick, temporarily
freezes and watches.*

TOM   Oh … my … God *(sniff)*. There might be a
        shorter one. Keep going, keep picking, I
        might have just got a slightly *(sniff)* short   85
        one when there's a really short one. *(snort)*
        Keep going. This one isn't that short. It's not
        much shorter than yours, Neil. *(holding his
        short straw between thumb and finger he insists
        on measuring it against all the others picked
        from here on)*

        *Andrew picks a long straw which Tom instantly
        measures against his own straw.*

ANDREW Sorry, mate. *(he turns away and smiles quietly
        to himself, relieved)*

NIGEL   *(he picks a long straw, measures it against
        Tom's)* It's you, Snotty Tom.   90

        *Forgetting their earlier sulk, Liam and Stuart rush
        to pick, delighted that Tom has got the short
        straw.*

STUART *(he picks a long straw)* It *is* you, Snotty Tom.

LIAM   *(he picks a long straw and hugs Tom violently)*
        It's you, it's you, it's *you*!

        *Tom sinks into a chair and looks horrified. Andrew
        quietly consoles him. The girls' queue starts
        moving again. Katie picks a long straw.*

KATIE   Hey, Hattie, d'you remember at Primary
        when Billy Crunch stole Miss Anil's purse?

        Hattie is poised to pick.

HATTIE *(sarcastic)* Oh, thanks, Katie. I'm about to   95

get sent to thieve some biscuits and you
remind me of the only boy who ever got
expelled in the history of Heath Lane
Primary. Brilliant. Whatever happened to
Billy Crunch?   100

KATIE   I think he ended up working for his dad …
But then they got caught.

Hattie picks a long straw.

BRIONY   If we'd gone up first, we'd have picked by
now. I told you we should have gone up at
the start.   105

RONI   It won't be you, Briony. It'll be me. I know
it'll be me.

LISA   Alison, Kayleigh, have you picked yet? Come
on, you're going to be last. Come on.

*Briony picks a long straw. So does Roni. There are
two straws left – and only Kayleigh and Alison left
to pick.*

KAYLEIGH   I've told you. I'm not going. I'm not even   110
picking a stupid straw. I'm not. I'm not even
getting out of my chair. D'you think I'll get
out of my chair? I'm not. I'm not even getting
out of my chair … *(repeat to fade)*

*Alison edges reluctantly forward. Her hand hovers
between the two straws. Kayleigh watches intently
while pretending to examine her nails and look
out of the window. Alison picks. It's the short
straw.*

ALISON   *(cold, numb)* My mum is going to kill me …   115

Scene 13

Tom and Alison become the central focus of the class. They slump into seats, side by side, alternately burying their faces in their hands and looking terrified.

ALISON   I can't do it. I can't. I've never stolen anything in my life.

BRIONY   You stole my rubber in Year 3, Alison.

ALISON   I did NOT!

BRIONY   *(quietly to Roni)* She did. *(shrugs, lets it go)*

LIAM   *(leaping at Tom and Alison)* Right, Snotty Tom,   5
Alison, you *heroes* – here's the plan. *(pause, looks around for help)* What *is* the plan? We need a plan.

DAN   OK. One of you's ill. Really ill.

TOM   Me. I feel sick …   10

DAN   Yeah, that's good, Tom. You look sick. Try looking sicker. *(Tom pulls a face)* Even sicker.

ROBBIE   Hold your stomach. *(he does)* Groan a bit. *(he does, like a creaking door)* Louder. *(he growls)*

DAN   Good enough. Right, Alison. Snotty Tom's   15
ill. You need to take him to the office to see Mrs Dixon—

ANDREW   *(theatrically)* The dragon that guards the biscuits that are rightfully ours!

DAN   That's the one. And when she takes Snotty   20
Tom for a little lie down in the first aid room, you open the cupboard behind her desk, grab the tin of biscuits—

ALISON	The big tin of biscuits? The big, huge tin of biscuits? And do what with them? Stuff them 25 up my jumper?
DAN	Oh.
NEIL	Take your bag with you. Your rucksack. Plenty of room in there.
ALISON	Why would I do that? Why would I take my 30 rucksack to the office?
NIGEL	Oh, you can't leave it in here. It's got valuables in it, I expect. Someone might go through it and steal stuff.
DAN	Good point. OK? All sorted, then. 35
TOM	*(sarcastically)* Oh I had no idea it would be so easy.
DAN	Empty your bag out, Alison. Make room for the treasure. *(she does, neatly laying it all out on her desk)*
ALISON	And what about when they ask what lesson 40 I've brought him out of? And the teacher's name?
GEMMA	It's a supply teacher. You haven't had them before. You don't know their name.
ALISON	Oh, you've got an answer for everything, 45 haven't you? But it's not you that's got to go and stick a huge tin of biscuits in your rucksack while—
LIAM	Ooh, she used to be so nice and quiet. Anything wrong, love? 50

Alison glares at him.

GEMMA   Look, it'll be fine. If Mrs Dixon's out of the way, you shove the biscuits in your rucksack. If she isn't, you don't. You come back without them and it's no problem.

LIAM   Except we don't get any biscuits—   55

STUART   And everyone hates you.

GEMMA   *(comfortingly)* No, they don't. What is it that fat walrus PE teacher always says?

LIAM   *(a suggestion)* 'Why is it your time of the month twice as often as all the other girls,   60 Gemma?'

GEMMA   No, not that. He says … 'It's not the winning, it's the taking part.'

LIAM   No guts, no glory!

STUART   No biscuits, no glory!   65

GEMMA   All set then?

Tom stands to join Alison, looking like a condemned man about to be hanged.

DAN   So remember, Tom – stomach, face, groan. Alison – biscuit tin in the cupboard, biscuit tin in the rucksack.

ALISON   *(picking up her large rucksack)* Can we   70 practise? I mean, how big is this tin of biscuits?

Dan uses his hands to demonstrate an average-sized biscuit tin.

ALISON   What if it won't fit in my rucksack?

CRAIG   If it'll fit your pencil case and your collection of gel pens, it'll fit a tin of biscuits.   75

ALISON   *(sounding increasingly desperate)* And what do
          I say when I get there?

GEMMA   You just say … *(posh voice)* I'm terribly sorry
          to trouble you, Mrs Dixon … Say it after me.

ALISON   I'm terribly sorry to trouble you, Mrs Dixon …   80

GEMMA   But Thomas is suffering from a most terrible
          sickness …

ALISON   But Thomas is suffering from—

GEMMA   *(grinning)* No, not really! You just say Tom's
          not feeling well and the teacher asked you   85
          to take him to the office.

ALISON   *(running this through to herself with a range of
          intonation)* Tom's not well. The teacher asked
          me to take him to the office. Tom's not well.
          The teacher asked him to take me to the
          office. He's not well. Tom asked the office   90
          to take me to the teacher …

GEMMA   OK? Off you go then!

          *Tom and Alison take a step towards the classroom
          door – and stop.*

TOM   But what if—

          *Gemma silences him with a gentle touch of her
          finger to his lips.*

GEMMA   It'll be fine. Just walk out the door, keep
          walking and it'll just happen. OK?   95

          *The whole class gather round them by the
          classroom door to wave them off. Pats on the
          back, hugs, salutes and 'good lucks' from all.
          Reluctantly, and with a shove, they leave.*

Scene 14

Nigel and Katie rush to the window.

KATIE   They're walking down the corridor … past
        Room 21, Room 20 … past the library …

CRAIG   How can you see them from there, Katie?

KATIE   I can't, idiot. It's called *imagination*. And
        they're just coming through the doors, into   5
        sight … *now. (pause)* … *now. (pause)* They're
        out. They're in the playground.

Nigel and others rush to the window to watch.

NIGEL   They're crossing the playground, heading for
        the double doors!

GEMMA   Anyone around, Nigel?   10

NIGEL   No. Oh! Bonnington's come out the double
        doors. The fat PE bloke. He's walking across
        the playground towards them. He's smiling.
        He's eating a sausage roll.

NEIL   And ketchup? Got it all down himself?   15

NIGEL   Can't see from here. Need binoculars. He's
        smiling at them. He's still smiling at them.
        He's opening his mouth … He's going to say
        something to them … No, he's having a bite
        of his sausage roll … He's walked past them!   20

Silent cheers around the classroom.

KATIE   Nearly at the doors … nearly … nearly …
        (pause) They're in!

More silent cheers.

KATIE   They'll be walking down the corridor to the

office ... *(she starts walking on the spot, miming their progress)* turning left ... *(she does)* through the door ... *(still miming)* ... and they're in the office.   25

LIAM   *(mimicking Alison's earlier practice)* Sorry to trouble you Mrs Dixon, but can I stick your biscuit tin in my rucksack?   30

Laughter – and then a lull.

STUART   So ... what do we do now?

GEMMA   We wait.

Scene 15

A general staring into space. Some anxious pacing to the window, looking, seeing nothing. Some whispering.

Kayleigh rummages quite urgently in her bag and finds a water bottle. She drains it greedily. She is looking tired and slightly anxious.

STUART   I tell you what would be well nice with a biscuit ...

LIAM   What?

STUART   ... don't mind which ...

LIAM   *(louder, more urgent)* What?

STUART   Bourbon ... custard cream ... pink wafer ...   5
I don't mind.

LIAM   *(even louder)* What would be well nice with a biscuit?

STUART   *(dreamily)* A large ... hot ... steaming ... cup of tea.   10

LIAM	*(in disbelief)* A cup of tea? Tea?!
STUART	*(still dreaming)* Yeah. Tea. And two sugars.
LIAM	*(increasingly sarcastically)* We'll nip down the staff room and pinch a kettle then shall we?
STUART	Yeah!
LIAM	And a carton of milk.
STUART	Yeah!!
LIAM	And twenty-five teabags. And a bag of sugar.
STUART	Yeah!!
LIAM	And twenty-five mugs. And a really big teapot.
STUART	We could share …
LIAM	And a teaspoon. And put it all in your rucksack.
STUART	I haven't got a rucksack. I haven't got a school bag.
LIAM	Oh, shame! It's all off then, Stuart. And it was *such* a good idea.

15

20

25

Alone at the back of the classroom, Kayleigh is looking increasingly tired and anxious.

KAYLEIGH	*(faintly)* Anyone got a drink I can nick a bit of?

She is ignored.

NIGEL	I like a can of coke with a biscuit.
NEIL	Hey, you know that coke machine – used to be in the hall before we all got healthy and they took it away?
LIAM	Yeah, I've been eating a lot of lettuce lately. And kiwi fruit.

30

35

NEIL   You know where that coke machine went?
They've got it in the staff room. Baggy told
me. How's that fair? We're not allowed it and
a bunch of fat teachers are tipping it down
their—   40

LIAM   Let's go and nick the coke machine out of
the staff room! We'll put it on a little trolley
and wheel it through the school and no one
will ever notice.

*Kayleigh is beginning to sway slightly in her chair.
She stands up unsteadily.*

KAYLEIGH   *(decisively)* I need to go to the office.   45

Scene 16

GEMMA   Eh? What do you need to go to the office for,
Kayleigh?

KAYLEIGH   I just need to go to the office.

DAN   Alison and Snotty Tom have gone. To nick
the biscuits. Weren't you here a minute ago?   5
Didn't you notice? You can't go to the office
as well.

KAYLEIGH   I need to go to the office.

*Kayleigh is looking increasingly unwell. She is
swaying, sweating, looking very tired and pale.*

KATIE   *(approaching her, concerned)* What's the
matter, Kayleigh?   10

KAYLEIGH   Nothing. I just need to go to the office.

KATIE   Are you sick? Don't you feel well?

KAYLEIGH   I'm fine. I just need to go to the office.

| ROBBIE | *(to Andrew)* You can see she's not well. Look at her. | 15 |

| ANDREW | She can't stand up straight. What's the matter with her? | |

| GEMMA | Oh brilliant. We've sent a couple of fakers to the office saying they're not well and now we've got a real one. You can't go to the office, Kayleigh. They'll think something's up. We'll get found out. | 20 |

| KAYLEIGH | *(moving uncertainly towards the door)* I've got to go to the office. That's all. | |

Kayleigh is oblivious to everyone in the class looking at and whispering about her.

| GEMMA | *(worried)* Look. Sit down. Have a drink of water. *(she eases her forcefully into a chair)* | 25 |

| KAYLEIGH | *(trying to stand up)* I don't need a drink of water. I need to go to the office. | |

| GEMMA | *(firmly)* Stay there. Don't move. Lisa, keep an eye on her. *(aside)* And don't let her go. | 30 |

Lisa stands guard over her. Katie, Hattie, and Laura B gather and try to comfort her.

| KAYLEIGH | *(angry but weak)* I don't need to sit down. I need to go to the office. | |

Gemma huddles with Liam, Stuart, and Robbie.

| GEMMA | She can't go. If there's two kids from our lesson already ill in the office, that office woman'll suspect something. She'll start talking to teachers. Someone'll come. | 35 |

ROBBIE	But if she's ill … I mean, she looks ill. She looks *really* ill.
GEMMA	She's *got* to stay here. At least until Alison and Snotty Tom get back. Maybe we can 40 sort her out. Just until the end of the lesson. I've got some paracetamol in my bag.

Gemma fetches the paracetamol from her bag and takes them to Kayleigh.

STUART	She's faking, I reckon.
LIAM	*(nodding)* Attention seeking.

Robbie looks doubtful. The group break up and gather with Kayleigh.

GEMMA	Got you some paracetamol. OK? 45
KAYLEIGH	*(desperate and angry)* I don't want paracetamol. I haven't got a headache. I need to go to the office.
GEMMA	What's wrong then? What's the matter?
KAYLEIGH	Nothing! 50

Pause. Silence.

KAYLEIGH	*(reluctant and quiet)* I'm diabetic.

The news goes round the room in whispers. Everyone is surprised.

GEMMA	What does that mean? I mean, I know what it means, but what do we do? What do you need?
KAYLEIGH	I skipped breakfast. I need some juice or 55 something. A drink. Something sweet. With sugar. Not diet.

GEMMA	*(to Kayleigh)* Why didn't you say? *(to the class)* Right. Who's got a packed lunch?
NEIL	I ate mine on the way to school. 60

Andrew, Robbie, Darren, Katie, Hattie and Sara start rummaging in their bags, pulling out sandwiches, lunchboxes, etc., searching.

GEMMA	We need some juice. Or a drink. Not diet. With sugar.
KATIE	*(up)* I've got juice. *(down)* But it's diet.
HATTIE	I've got water.
SARA	I've got … *(rummaging, produces)* yoghurt! 65 With crunchy bits …
ROBBIE	I've got orange juice. *(he brings it to Kayleigh, opens it, she drinks)*

All watch closely.

KAYLEIGH	Can you lot stop staring and leave me alone? It's like being a monkey in the flamin' zoo.
LIAM	Yeah, she's definitely feeling better. 70
ROBBIE	I think she's back to normal.
LISA	It's like magic! A magic potion!

Kayleigh finishes the drink.

KAYLEIGH	Anyone got a sandwich I can have? Or some fruit?
LIAM	*(horrified)* Fruit? 75
SARA	I've got a sandwich. *(she peels it apart)* Cheese and … oh my God, Mum, what is that red stuff? *(showing it to Hattie)* What *is*

that? Why has she put it in there? It looks
like roadkill.

ANDREW   I've got a banana. Here. *(he gives it to*   80
Kayleigh, she eats)

LIAM   Fruit?

KAYLEIGH   People do eat it, you know.

GEMMA   Better now?

KAYLEIGH   *(still defiant)* I'm fine. *(shyly, reluctantly)* Thanks.

GEMMA   S'alright. What happens if you don't get   85
juice and stuff when … *that* happens?

KAYLEIGH   Ambulance.

KATIE   I never knew you were diabetic.

KAYLEIGH   And you still don't. And if you tell anyone,
you'll be in an ambulance. OK?   90

Katie nods.

Scene 17

NIGEL   *(at the window)* They're coming back! Snotty
Tom and Alison. They're coming back!

DAN   *(hurrying to the window)* Have they got it,
Nige? Have they got the biscuit tin?

Several others follow him to the window, peering out.

NIGEL   I can't see it. She's got her rucksack on,   5
though. They're halfway across the playground.

LIAM   Has the rucksack got anything in it?

DAN   Can't see. They're walking fast, though.

LIAM   Scared. Doesn't mean they've got them,
though.   10

NIGEL	They've cleared the playground … coming through the doors.

| KATIE | *(imagining again)* Walking down the corridor … past the library … Room 20, Room 21 … and should be walking in here any second— 15 |

The door opens. Tom and Alison enter looking pale, shell-shocked but excited. They slump in chairs.

| LIAM | And? |

Scene 18

GEMMA	What happened? What happened?
TOM	Give us a minute.

He breathes heavily, composing himself. Starting slowly, panting and nervous, Tom and Alison's story gathers pace and enthusiasm. It becomes a re-enactment with Tom taking the role of Mrs Dixon as well as himself. The rest of the class gather in a line behind and either side of the teacher's desk as an audience.

LIAM	You didn't get them, did you?
ALISON	*(ignoring him)* So, we walk in, and Mrs Dixon's sitting behind her desk. 5
DAN	Like she always is.

Tom sits at the teacher's desk assuming the role of Mrs Dixon. Perhaps he borrows a pair of glasses from another student which he wears when playing the part of Mrs Dixon and removes when being himself.

ALISON   Yeah. So we walk in and she says—

TOM   *(as Mrs Dixon)* And *why* are you two students not in your lesson?

GEMMA   *(not surprised)* That's what she always says.   10

ALISON   And I can see the cupboard behind her – the one with the biscuits in.

Dan arranges a student desk to be the cupboard. He grabs a packed lunch box still lying around after the Kayleigh incident and shows the class.

DAN   Biscuits. *(he deliberately places it 'in the cupboard' to be the biscuit tin)*

ALISON   The doors were shut – so I didn't even know if they were in there.   15

Dan grabs Hattie and Katie to play the parts of the cupboard doors. He stands them either side of the desk, and deliberately 'closes' them.

GEMMA   And you said?

ALISON   And I said, 'Sorry to bother you Mrs Dixon, but the teacher's sent me with Tom. He doesn't feel well.' And Tom's standing there, holding his tummy and groaning a bit …   20
(she drags Tom from behind the desk to be himself) … holding his tummy and groaning a bit … *(after another nudge, Tom enters into the spirit of the performance and does so)* … and she looks really cross and says—

TOM   *(sitting behind the desk again, as Mrs Dixon)* Which teacher?

ALISON	And I said, 'I don't know, Miss, it's a supply. 25 I think Miss Barraclough's ill.' And she believed me! And she says—
TOM	*(as Mrs Dixon)* It's Tom, isn't it? Is it your sinuses again? Have you got *another* headache?
	(as himself) And I'm standing there, holding 30 my tummy and groaning. *(he does)*
DAN	So what did you do?

Tom grabs his head and carries on groaning.

GEMMA	What did she say?
ALISON	Nothing. Just goes—
TOM	*(back behind desk as Mrs Dixon, suspicious)* Hmmm. 35
ALISON	And it goes all quiet. *(pause)* And she says—
TOM	*(as Mrs Dixon, briskly)* Well I can't give you anything for it. You know that don't you?
ALISON	And I said, 'Tom thought a glass of water might make him feel better. And he thought 40 if he could lie down for five minutes in the first aid room.' And she looks at him … *(behind the desk, Tom glares at her)* … and looks … and looks … and finally she says—
TOM	*(as Mrs Dixon)* Come along then. 45
ALISON	And she takes him into the first aid room.

Meanwhile, Dan has opened the doors of the metal storage cupboard, and is beckoning to Tom. With one door open, this will represent the first aid room. Tom hides behind the cupboard door.

TOM	And gets me a glass of water.

ALISON	So I'm standing in the office, by myself, looking at this cupboard with the biscuits in—
GEMMA	And? 50
ALISON	And I can't move. I tried! I thought: just put one foot forward and then the other and then another …
GEMMA	And?
ALISON	And I couldn't move. 55
GEMMA	And?
ALISON	And the phone starts ringing.
DAN	Ring, ring! Ring, ring!
TOM	And she comes charging out of the first aid room and answers it. 60

Dan hurriedly places a pencil case on Mrs Dixon's desk to be the phone.

TOM *(as Mrs Dixon, picking up the phone/pencil case)* Hello? *(pause)* Well I'm rather busy at the moment. Is it urgent? *(pause)* Are you sure? *(pause)* Very well then, hold on. *(she slams the phone/pencil case onto the desk)*

So she disappears into that room at the back … *(he disappears through the crowd of students behind the desk; one of them rattles chairs and paper to signify Mrs Dixon's searching)* … and 65 starts rattling around with filing cabinets and stuff.

ALISON And Tom's leaning out the first aid room *(he does)* watching me doing nothing and trying to get me to move … 70

TOM	*(loud whisper)* Go on, get them out the cupboard!
ALISON	And I finally make myself move. I go behind her desk, open the cupboard *(she does)*, get the tin out and put it on her desk … *(she does)*
TOM	And Mrs Dixon comes back. 75

He re-enters through the crowd of students. Alison stands between Tom/Mrs Dixon and the tin of biscuits, shielding it from her view. Mrs Dixon moves round the desk. Alison moves round the desk, smiling, still shielding the tin.

Tom/Mrs Dixon picks up the phone/pencil case.

TOM	*(as Mrs Dixon)* I can't find them. I'll have to call you back. Yes, before lunchtime. *(puts phone down)* Now. What are you—
ALISON	*(very proudly)* And just as she's going to start asking me questions that I can't answer, 80 Tom saves me!
TOM	*(behind his hand)* Mrs Dixon, I think I'm going to be sick!
ALISON	So she runs off to see Tom in the first aid room *(Tom does)* and all I can hear is— 85
TOM	*(as Mrs Dixon)* There are some bowls in here somewhere. Don't be sick till I've found one. They're always on this shelf. Who's been in here, moving things? Try to keep calm.
ALISON	And just as I'm going to stuff the tin in my 90 rucksack, guess who appears?
GEMMA	Who?
ALISON	Mr Bonnington.

DAN   Hold on! *(he stuffs his coat up his school sweatshirt, grabs a sandwich out of a packed lunch box and appears at Mrs Dixon's desk, impersonating Mr Bonnington, waddling and spraying sandwich crumbs as he speaks)* Mrs Dixon? Mrs Dixon?   95

ALISON   'She's in the first aid room,' I say. So he wanders in, nicely blocking the whole doorway *(Dan does)* and all you can hear is Tom shouting—

TOM   I can't keep it down much longer,   100 Mrs Dixon! I'm gonna spew!

ALISON   And Mrs Dixon turning the place upside down looking for a bowl *(students rattle chairs, etc. to simulate the chaos)* and Mr Bonnington asking Mrs Dixon for   105 something and her shouting back at him …

DAN   *(as Mr Bonnington)* Have you got a spare sandwich, Mrs Dixon? Or a sausage roll? Any ketchup?

TOM   I'm gonna spew, Mrs Dixon. I can't hold   110 on anymore!

Dan and Tom keep the chaos going, but not so loudly that we can' t hear Alison.

DAN   I suppose a full English breakfast is out of the question?

TOM   Please hurry up, Mrs Dixon!

ALISON   So I try to jam the biscuit tin into my   115 rucksack … *(she wrestles with it for a short while)* but it won't go … and then I realise. It'd be better not to take the tin. So I take the lid off, tip the biscuits into my rucksack, put the tin back in the cupboard. Easy! So 120 I wait. And I wait. And then I say 'Mrs Dixon, could you tell Tom I'm going to go back to my lesson?' And suddenly it all goes quiet … *(it does)* … and I hear Tom say—

TOM Actually, I feel much better now Mrs Dixon. 125 I think I'd like to go back to my lesson, too.

ALISON And out comes Tom, and we leave. *(Tom emerges from the metal cupboard. Alison and Tom 'leave')*

GEMMA And what did Mrs Dixon do?

ALISON Don't know. Didn't look back.

Dan, as Mrs Dixon, emerges looking mystified from the cupboard.

And Tom says to me on the way back— 130

TOM You know she couldn't find a bowl for me to be sick in? *(he smiles and from under his sweatshirt, he pulls a pile of five or so cardboard, surgical bowls)* I thought it might help keep her busy …

ALISON So here we are. And here *(she rummages in* 135 *her rucksack)* is a custard cream. Anyone want one? Or a bourbon? Or a pink wafer?

The class gather round the rucksack, helping themselves to biscuits, quietly cheering and laughing. All as if in slow motion, Tom punches the air, mimes shouting for joy and runs into Alison's arms. Alison and Tom are hugged and patted, treated like heroes.

Act Two

Scene 1

Liam is standing on a desk. The rest of the class stand in a crowd at his feet – except Robbie, Andrew, Briony and Roni who sit prominently and despondently in a row at their desks, and Nigel who is again on lookout at the classroom door. Liam is clearly preparing to do something which is probably dangerous and definitely stupid.

LIAM	*(in a showman style)* Shall I?	
CROWD	Yes!	
LIAM	Are you ready?	
CROWD	Yes!	
ROBBIE	*(resignedly)* We're going to get done. We might as well be running up and down the corridor shouting 'Give me a detention! Keep me in at break! Expel me!'	5
LIAM	Are you sure?	
CROWD	Yes!	10
STUART	Oh get on with it!	
LIAM	Are you ready?	
CROWD	Yes!	
STUART	Yes, we're still ready.	
LIAM	Are you steady?	15
CROWD	Yes!	

Liam opens his mouth to speak but is interrupted.

NIGEL	Teacher!

The crowd disperse, flung into their seats as if on elastic. They sit still and try to look innocent, quiet and busy all at the same time. Liam is left standing on the desk, mouth still open. He can't believe his eyes.

LIAM   What are you *doing*?

They ignore him.

LIAM   If a teacher comes now, what are they gonna say? They don't care how good you're being   20
        now – you've spent half a lesson being bad.
        (laughs) The damage is done! There's no way out of it.

ROBBIE But there's slightly less chance of a teacher coming if you're not standing on a desk   25
        shouting as loud as you can.

BRIONY *(with terror as she realises)* Liam's right, it's too late to behave … we're doomed.

LIAM   *(grinning)* See, you should have thought of that earlier. At the start of the lesson.   30
        Before you decided you weren't going to tell the office we didn't have a teacher!

Still they wait, still Nigel watches, still Liam perches on the desktop waiting for his audience to return. He rolls his eyes in disgust at the class' timidity.

LIAM   *(climbing down from his desk and sprawling in a chair, mumbling)* Well, you've missed your chance. I'm not getting up there again.

Pause.

| STUART | *(whispers)* Who's out there, Nigel? | 35 |

NIGEL   *(whispers)* A man. In a suit. And a tie. I think he's … I think it's … All clear.

The class breathes a sigh of relief.

Scene 2

The class start to talk quietly, some whispering, still subdued by the threat of discovery. Liam prowls around looking dangerously bored and frustrated. Nigel ducks under his desk to retrieve his bag. It's missing. He wanders the room, looking under desks for it.

ANDREW   So what do we do now?

ROBBIE   Sit and wait to get caught. What else can we do? Sit in here like prisoners staring out of the window … the sun's shining and we have to sit here … like trapped rats …   5

ANDREW   At least we don't have to do any work …

ROBBIE   So what's the point of coming to school if you don't do any work? It's just pointless … sitting here … like trapped rats … like chickens waiting to be slaughtered … like   10 turkeys at Christmas … like …

ANDREW   OK, I think we get the picture.

Meanwhile, at a nearby desk …

ALISON   *(worried)* I can't believe we did it … I can't believe we stole …

TOM   *(triumphant)* No, me neither. We made a   15 good team, didn't we?

ALISON	My mum'll go ballistic if she ever finds out …	
TOM	*(laughs)* And mine.	
ALISON	I feel sick. Do you?	20
TOM	Little bit.	

ALISON I mean, it was exciting. And scary. And I felt so good when we came back … everyone cheering and being really happy with us. We'd done it and no one thought we would. 25 No one thought we *could*. Snotty Tom and Alison, they're just a pair of goody-goodies, send them out to steal stuff, they'll look really stupid …

TOM But we didn't. We did it. 30

ALISON But now all I can think about is whether we're going to get caught. I mean there's twenty people in here who know we did it. They're all going to tell someone, and someone'll tell someone else, and we'll get 35 found out and we'll get in really big trouble.

TOM I'm never doing anything like that again. Never. Never ever.

ALISON I mean, it felt great when we'd done it and 40 when we came back, being all … popular. But now, ten minutes later, it's all gone and forgotten – and you're just left with the taste of … the taste of …

TOM Biscuits? 45

ALISON Guilt.

Scene 3

NIGEL   *(still roaming)* Anyone seen my bag? It's not
funny …

ALISON   I just wish we'd gone and got a teacher. We
should have told the office at the start of the
lesson and got a teacher. Then none of this   5
would have happened. We're going to get
caught, I know we are. It's like waiting for …
waiting for … waiting for something that's
definitely going to happen.

LIAM   Oh, cheer up! If you never do anything   10
wrong in case you get caught, you'll never do
anything at all. Live a little. Hangman! Let's
play hangman.

ANDREW   *(to himself)* Now that's what I call living …

*While Liam rummages in the teacher's desk
drawers looking for a board pen, Nigel finds his
bag under Tom's desk and retrieves it.*

NIGEL   *(to Tom)* Did you put it there?   15

TOM   No!

NIGEL   Well, who did then? *(he returns to his desk and
begins looking for something in his bag)*

LIAM   *(finding a board pen, stands looking out at the
audience, as if looking at a whiteboard)* Right,
let's have a think … ermmm … *(smiles as a
good idea comes; starts setting out the 'blanks'
on the invisible whiteboard, pausing to spell out
the words on his fingers)*

STUART   You've spelt it wrong.   20

LIAM   How do you know? I can spell some words.

STUART	Only rude ones – and just 'cos you write them in the boys' toilets, doesn't mean you're spelling them right.
LIAM	*(finishing on the board)* OK. Who's playing? 25
STUART	Me. Erm … X.
LIAM	*(again, counting through the letters on his fingers)* No! No X in it. *(he draws the first line of the hanged man, smiling smugly)*
NIGEL	*(in his seat, rummaging in his bag)* Where is it?
DARREN	Where's what?
NIGEL	It was in here. I know it was. 30
DARREN	What was?
NIGEL	*(dramatically tipping the contents of his bag on the desk: books, packed lunch, tennis balls, etc.)* It's gone. It's not there. It's gone.
DARREN	What has?
NIGEL	My pencil case. Someone's been in my bag and taken it. 35
DARREN	You sure it was in there?
NIGEL	Positive. It had my dinner money in it. I put it in there this morning. My dinner money for the week. Ten quid.
STUART	Z. 40
LIAM	*(again, counting through the letters on his fingers)* Nope! *(purposefully adding to the hanged man)*
DARREN	Anyone seen Nigel's pencil case?
STUART	Q.
LIAM	You're not really trying, are you?

STUART   I am! I am!   45

Stuart grins behind his back as Liam turns back to the 'board' to add another line to the hanged man. But destroying any remaining interest in the game, Nigel, moving faster and faster, searches frantically around the classroom: under desks, behind the cupboard, on top of the cupboard, becoming increasingly desperate.

GEMMA   Oi! Nigel! What have you lost?

NIGEL   Pencil case.

GEMMA   What does it look like?

NIGEL   Blue. Kind of … *(indicates dimensions with his hands)* … with a zip on the top.   50

GEMMA   So … the size and shape of a pencil case, then. What was in it? A pen?

NIGEL   *(stating the obvious)* No!

GEMMA   Pencil?

NIGEL   *(still searching)* Might have been …   55

GEMMA   Ruler?

NIGEL   No …

GEMMA   Compass?

NIGEL   Don't think so …

GEMMA   Set square?   60

NIGEL   Dunno. What's that?

GEMMA   The triangle thing you get in maths sets. No one knows what they're really for. No one uses them till they lose their ruler.

NIGEL   Yeah! There *is* one of them!   65

GEMMA	So what's the fuss about? It's only a pencil case … and a pencil … and a set square.
NIGEL	And ten quid – my dinner money for the week.
GEMMA	*(suddenly understanding Nigel's worry)* Oh.

70

More people start to take an interest.

ALISON	Where did you leave it, Nigel?
NIGEL	It was in my bag.
CRAIG	Where was your bag?
NIGEL	It got nicked.
DARREN	He found it down there. *(points to under Tom's desk)*

75

CRAIG	But the pencil case had gone.
DARREN	And the tenner.

Nigel sags, hopelessly.

Scene 4

GEMMA	Did anyone see anything?

Lots of head shaking. No one saw anything.

NIGEL	*(mumbling sadly to himself)* All too busy stealing and eating biscuits … Everyone was all over the classroom … I was on lookout … should have kept an eye on my stuff …

5

LIAM	Right. We'll have to do a bag search.
GEMMA	Eh?
LIAM	A bag search. Got a problem with that? Something to hide?

GEMMA   *(affronted)* No! It's just … well … it's the   10
kind of thing teachers say, isn't it. Bit weird
hearing you say it …

LIAM   I might be a teacher when I'm older. *(teacher
voice)* Everyone tip your bags out on your
desks.   15

*They start to do so, some more reluctant than
others. Tom tips his bag out. From among his
belongings, he picks out a blue pencil case. He
realises with absolute horror that it is Nigel's.
Andrew notices, then Robbie, then his other
neighbours. Meanwhile …*

KAYLEIGH   I'm not tipping my bag out. There's private
stuff in it.

LIAM   Like what? Stolen goods? Jewels? A blue
pencil case?

*Gradually almost the whole class gathers round
Tom – including Liam, leaving Kayleigh talking to
herself. With a theatrical show of exasperation,
she tips her bag out.*

KAYLEIGH   And if anyone touches any of my stuff, I'll   20
mince 'em. Alright?

*But no one's interested. All look on accusingly at
Tom as he wordlessly mouths his shock, and his
innocence.*

TOM   But—

NIGEL   That's it! That's my pencil case!

TOM   But I—

NIGEL   Give it here.   25

TOM But—

Nigel grabs it, opens it, rummages, tips out a pencil and an angle measurer, turns it inside out.

GEMMA That's not a set square. It's not even a triangle shape! It's round! A circle! 30

NIGEL *(in disbelief)* My money's gone. Ten quid. Nicked.

As the silent, accusing stares increase in intensity, Tom becomes more and more alarmed.

TOM You don't think that I … *(pause)* I mean, I wouldn't … *(pause)* You know I wouldn't, 35
don't you Nigel?

NIGEL You stole a tin of biscuits.

TOM Alison stole the biscuits, I just—

ALISON Oh, thanks very much! Thank you!

DARREN And where did you find your bag, Nigel? 40

NIGEL Under Snotty Tom's desk.

DARREN Under Snotty Tom's desk. Exactly.

NIGEL *(accusing, finger pointed at Tom)* He nicked my bag, he took my pencil case out, and he took my money! 45

Scene 5

Whispers of surprise and accusation. Tom looks horrified, looks to Andrew and Robbie for support.

ROBBIE Hold on, hold on, Nigel. Just because Tom stole the biscuits, it doesn't mean he took

your money. You don't know it was Tom that
put your bag there, or took your pencil case,
or took your money. 5

TOM   We didn't steal the biscuits, anyway. We just
… took them.

LIAM   Yeah! You took them. You didn't pay for
them. They weren't yours. That woman
hasn't got them anymore. No one gave her   10
any money for them. Sounds to me like they
were stolen – and you did the stealing.

TOM   You ate them, Liam!

LIAM   *(feigning innocence)* When I ate those biscuits,
I had *no* idea they were stolen! If I'd known   15
I would never have touched—

TOM   Oh, shut up! Stealing biscuits isn't the same
as stealing money.

LIAM   That lady in the office paid money for the
biscuits – and you took them from her.   20
How much does a tin of biscuits cost?

STUART   About ten quid.

LIAM   Well, there you are then. It's *exactly* the
same as nicking Nigel's tenner – but in the
shape of delicious biscuits.   25

TOM   But stealing from the lady in the office isn't
the same as stealing from Nigel … he's a …
friend. Well, he's in my class. But he's not a
teacher, he's a … normal person.

DARREN   Well, he's a person, anyway. Almost.   30

LIAM   So what shall we do with him?

STUART   Report him to a teacher?

LIAM	Take him outside and kick him till he stops moving?
STUART	Stick drawing pins in him till he screams for mercy? 35
LIAM	And make him pay it back?
STUART	And be our slave for a day?
LIAM	A week!

Scene 6

ROBBIE	Nigel, who knew you had money in your pencil case? Who did you tell?
NIGEL	*(thinks)* No one. I didn't tell anyone.
ROBBIE	And when did you last see your bag?
NIGEL	*(thinks)* I brought it into reg. this morning, 5 put it under my desk … and the next time I saw it, it was under *his* desk.
ROBBIE	Did you go to your bag to look for anything during the lesson … like food or drink when Kayleigh was ill? 10
NIGEL	No. I haven't got any food or drink in my bag. That's why I've got a tenner in my pencil case – why I *had* a tenner – for my dinners. For the week. The whole week.
ROBBIE	So anyone could have moved your bag, 15 found your pencil case, found your money at any time during the lesson?
NIGEL	I s'pose.
ROBBIE	And the only people who haven't been here all lesson are Tom and Alison, right? 20
NIGEL	*(dubious)* Yeaaaah.

ROBBIE So they're the only ones with a bit of an alibi. That makes them the people *least* likely to have taken your money. Do you see?

NIGEL   But he could still have nicked it when he   25
was here. He's been here for most of the time, hasn't he? He hasn't got an able-bye for all the time, has he?

ANDREW Maybe we should search everyone's wallet and see who's got a tenner.   30

TOM   *(getting out his wallet very keenly)* Look! Nothing in it – just coins. Twenty ... thirty ... thirty-six pence.

LIAM   You're not going to put it in your wallet! It'll be down his sock or ... somewhere   35
else that nobody's going to want to go looking.

LAURA B Hang on! Wait a minute! Earlier on, when you lot were all ... talking about ... something ... I was listening. Listening to   40
Sara and Daisy. Talking. About money.

Scene 7

The entire cast freezes, except Laura B, Sara and Daisy, who have their conversation in flashback. Laura drops in and out of the action, either listening or narrating.

LAURA B Sara was saying something about ... something, when all of a sudden she says:

SARA   Daisy, can you lend me a fiver?

DAISY   What for?

| SARA | It's really important. I'll give it you back by the end of the week. | 5 |

SARA It's really important. I'll give it you back by the end of the week.

DAISY What is it? What's wrong?

SARA I … can't tell you. It's a … surprise. Can you lend it? It's really important.

Sara and Daisy freeze.

Scene 8

LAURA B See? See what I mean?

The class unfreeze. Accusing stares and whispers.

SARA So? I wanted to borrow five quid. So what if I did?

LAURA B Well you wanted money, didn't you? For a surprise, you said. For something *important*. For something so important you'd *steal* for it?

SARA 'Course I didn't steal it! I didn't even know that Nigel had a tenner in his—

DAISY 'Course she didn't steal it!

LAURA B Maybe she didn't. But that's not all. Is it, Daisy?

All except Laura B freeze.

Scene 9

LAURA B That wasn't where their little chat ended. 'Cos Daisy goes—

Daisy and Sara unfreeze.

DAISY I would lend it, mate. But I've only got a tenner. Have you got five quid change?

SARA   If I had five quid change, I wouldn't need   5
         to borrow five quid, would I, stoopid?!

Daisy and Sara freeze.

LAURA B So, Daisy's got a tenner, has she? Well, where
         did she get that from, I wonder?

Scene 10

*Everyone unfreezes. More accusing stares and
whispers.*

DAISY   I got it off my mum yesterday, alright? She
         always gives me a tenner at the weekend.
         Pocket money.

SARA   You're just trying to get us into trouble 'cos
         you're not coming to Daisy's dad's in the   5
         holidays, aren't you? You just think you're
         getting Daisy back, don't you?! *(going for
         Laura B)* And me, 'cos I'm going and you're
         not 'cos you're such a cow, you—

GEMMA   *(restraining her)* Hold it, hold it, no one's   10
         saying either of you nicked Nigel's tenner.

LAURA B I am.

GEMMA   No, you're not.

DAISY   For all we know, *she (indicates Laura B)* nicked
         it and she's trying to get the blame put on   15
         us.

Laura B lunges at Daisy. Others restrain her.

GEMMA   OK, OK, we're just thinking about what
         might have happened to the money so we
         can find it and give it back to Nigel and

everyone can live happily ever after. Alright? 20
I bet loads of people in the class have got a
tenner on them. *(turning to appeal to the class)*

Everyone looks at everyone else.

LIAM   I've got a tenner. In my wallet.

GEMMA   D'you know what's strange? A while ago,
when Nigel first noticed his pencil case was 25
missing, who was it who said, 'Let's do a bag
search'?

LIAM   Me. Why?

GEMMA   I thought it was weird at the time.

LISA   You said it was weird, didn't you, Gemma? 30
You said it sounded like something a teacher
would say, didn't you Gemma?

GEMMA   Shuttup, Lisa.

LIAM   So?

GEMMA   So, let's just say it was Liam that nicked the 35
money …

LIAM   No. Let's not just say that. Let's just say Liam
cleaned his dad's car at the weekend and got
paid a tenner for it.

GEMMA   *(pondering on, regardless)* Let's just say it was 40
Liam that took Nigel's pencil case, nicked the
tenner and dumped the pencil case in Snotty
Tom's bag. What would be the best way to
get everyone to think Snotty Tom had done
it? 45

LISA   Do a bag search. So we'd find the pencil
case in Snotty Tom's bag.

GEMMA   *(eyebrows raised)* Clever.

LIAM   *(mainly angry, slightly desperate)* I tell you
        what, Nigel, this money you lost. What did   50
        it look like? Can you describe it?

NIGEL   Yeah. It was a tenner.

LIAM   But what did it look like?

NIGEL   Well, it was about … *(indicates dimensions
        with his hands)* … er … brown …   55

LIAM   *(pulling a ten pound note out of his wallet)* And
        did it look like … *(with a flourish)* this?

NIGEL   Yes.

LIAM   *(with heavy sarcasm)* Oh, well then. It must
        have been me. Call the police. Ring my   60
        lawyer. Get me a cell ready. I'm nicked. Look,
        just 'cos I get in trouble at school—

STUART And out of school.

LIAM   Shuttup, Stuart. Just 'cos I get in trouble
        sometimes, it doesn't mean I'm a thief.   65

STUART You are, though.

LIAM   Shuttup, Stuart. It doesn't mean that
        everything that happens is my fault. God, the
        one time I come to school and a teacher
        doesn't turn up to hassle me for something   70
        I haven't done, then you lot start doing it! I
        didn't nick his money. Alright? You don't
        thieve from a mate, do you?

GEMMA   Is Nigel your mate? Nigel, do you know this
        boy? Do you know his name?   75

        Nigel nods but is embarrassed.

LIAM   Alright, alright … I admit … I took his pencil
case. I found it on the floor, I knew it was
his, and I bunged it in someone else's bag. I
didn't know whose it was, but I bunged it in
there. It was a joke, alright?   80

GEMMA   Ha ha.

LIAM   OK, not the funniest joke ever, but a joke.
And then Nigel started flapping and
panicking about his stupid pencil case and I
couldn't remember where I'd put it so I said   85
let's have a bag search so it'd get found and
the stupid joke would be over. But I did NOT
steal anything out of the pencil case. Alright?

*Silence. A space appears around Liam as
everyone, except Stuart, moves away.*

Scene 11

*Andrew and Robbie gather round Tom to support
him.*

ROBBIE   Well, that's narrowed it down then. Currently
on the list of suspects are … *(he writes a list
in the back of an exercise book)* … Tom …
because the pencil case was found in his
bag …   5

TOM   Are you writing my name down? Cross it out.
Rub it out now. You know I didn't do it.

ROBBIE   It's only a list … I'm not going to show it to
the police. So … Liam … because he's got a
ten pound note in his wallet and he admits   10
he put the pencil case in Tom's bag … and

Daisy because according to Laura B she said she needed money for something important … Sara because she admitted she'd got a ten pound note … and Laura B because she 15 accused Daisy and Sara. Or it could be anyone else who's been in this room for the last forty minutes. So … who was it?

ANDREW Well, I think it was Tom. Joke! I don't know. Liam seems a pretty obvious choice. But 20 who's going to tell him that?

Scene 12

STUART (grinning) So, was it you?

LIAM No!

STUART Really?

LIAM No!

STUART No, really, was it? 5

LIAM No!

STUART Yeah, but really, was it you?

LIAM No, I did not steal his stupid freakin' money, OK?

STUART Whoa, OK, I was only asking … (pause) … 10 but it was you, wasn't it?

Scene 13

DAISY (to Laura E) I can't believe you just stood there while she was accusing me!

SARA And me. I stood up for you, Daisy, didn't I?

LAURA E   I … I didn't know what to say. I couldn't
           believe she was saying it. The little … cow!   5
           I'm never speaking to her again.

Scene 14

Nigel sits at his desk looking worried. Dan
approaches. As he talks, interest gathers.

DAN   You know, Nige, I've been thinking. If Liam
       put your pencil case in Snotty Tom's bag,
       someone else could have gone in there and
       taken your money. *(pause while this sinks in,*
       then secretively) I caught Ben going through   5
       my pencil case the other day.

NIGEL   Ben? He's weird …

Ben approaches.

DAN   Yeah. I said to him, 'What are you doing?' He
       said he was looking for a pen – he wanted to
       borrow a pen.   10

BEN   Yeah, well I was. So?

DAN   All I'm saying is … maybe you wanted to
       borrow a pen today. Maybe you were looking
       through Nigel's pencil case, looking for a pen
       to borrow, and you found a crisp ten pound   15
       note. And maybe, just maybe, you borrowed
       that instead.

BEN   Yeah and what would I want a pen for? We
       haven't had to do much writing so far this
       lesson. Had you noticed? We haven't got a   20
       teacher. Why would I want a pen? Do you
       think I was writing my diary? Making a

shopping list? And if I was looking for a pen,
d'you think I'd look in Nigel's pencil case?
He's never got a pen.   25

DAN   Yeah, but you didn't know it was Nigel's
pencil case, did you?

BEN   Eh?

DAN   Well, where did you find the pencil case?

BEN   I didn't find the pencil case. I didn't touch   30
the pencil case.

DAN   Alright, but where was the pencil case when
the tenner went missing? It wasn't in Nigel's
bag. It was in Snotty Tom's bag. And Snotty
Tom's always got a pen. Sometimes, he's got 35
two or three pens. If I wanted to borrow a
pen, I'd ask Snotty Tom. So maybe you
thought you'd have a look for a pen in Snotty
Tom's bag, in what you thought was Snotty
Tom's pencil case and maybe you found a   40
ten pound note. Eh? Eh?

ALISON Craig was looking in my pencil case earlier.

CRAIG   So?

ALISON So maybe you looked in Nigel's pencil case,
as well. If you don't mind going through my   45
stuff, then maybe you went through his stuff
too.

CRAIG   *(in disbelief)* You were watching me when I
looked in your pencil case. If I was going to
nick something out of it, I might have   50
waited till you weren't looking, maybe?

BEN   *(to Dan)* So, because I was looking in your
pencil case a few days ago, that means I stole

Nigel's money? I look in a pencil case – once
– and I'm a thief? Oh, blame me for   55
everything. That big boat that sank … hit an
iceberg … years ago …

DAN   The *Titanic*?

BEN   Yeah, that was me. Put an iceberg where it
shouldn't have been. World War Two? That   60
was me. Me and Hitler, we were like that
(crosses fingers). He did everything I told
him. Sucker! And the war before that …
what was it called?

DAN   World War One?   65

BEN   Me. I started that. Nicked a tenner off this
German … turned into a fight … just got a
bit out of hand. Global warming? Me, me,
me. All of it. Blame Ben, he's weird, it'll be
his fault.   70

Dan is silent, embarrassed and confused.

DAN   I'm not saying it was you. I'm just saying …

BEN   Yeah, there's a lot of people saying a lot of
things about a lot of people. Look at us –
the accused. Snotty Tom's there with his
friends. Liam with his. Daisy and Sara with   75
their friends … Where's all my friends,
gathering round? *(he looks at the empty
space around him)* Where are they, telling
me they know it wasn't me, that I'm not
that kind of person? Are they under here?   80
(he looks under a desk) Here? *(he lifts a chair
and looks under it)* No, I don't think they are.
'Cos the freak hasn't got anyone who'll

stand up for him. Has he? *(he turns and sits, facing away)*

LISA What's he on about? 85

GEMMA He says he didn't take Nigel's money.

LISA Oh.

Scene 15

NEIL How long's left of this lesson?

DARREN Why?

NEIL Just wondering.

DARREN Wondering what?

NEIL Oh, you know, the usual things … will we 5
get done for spending the lesson without a
teacher … will Mrs Dixon notice her biscuits
have gone missing … who's got Nigel's
tenner … will he get it back … you know,
the usual stuff. 10

DARREN About ten minutes.

NIGEL *(sadly)* I was going to have a sausage roll at
break. I'm gonna be starving now. I'm gonna
be starving all week … 'cos of one of you.

*Suspicious glances around at the suspects: Tom,
Sara, Daisy, Laura, Liam, Ben.*

SARA *(shouts)* Don't look at me! I never took your 15
money!

DAISY *(shouts)* You can look in my bag … *(empties
it)* … my purse … *(empties it)* … I haven't got
your money, alright?

LIAM What about your coat? 20

DAISY	Fine! *(she grabs it and throws it at him)* Search it!
LIAM	*(calm)* It's always the guilty one who shouts the loudest …
SARA	Oh, shut up. Everyone knows it was you!
BEN	You know what we should do.

25

LIAM	Oh, was it? Was it me? Come and search me then *(winks)*.
BEN	*(louder)* I said, you know what we should do?
SARA	Not without a pair of rubber gloves.
BEN	*(louder still)* I said, you know what we should do?

30

SARA	*(snaps)* What? What should we do, weirdo?
BEN	Have a whip-round.

Silence.

SARA	Eh?
BEN	We should have a whip-round. Everyone puts in, I dunno, 10p. To pay for Nigel's lunch. 10p's not much, is it? To help him out.

35

SARA	I'm not putting in 10p 'cos Liam's nicked his dinner money.
BEN	It doesn't matter who's nicked it. He hasn't got any money. He's hungry. So we all put in 10p. It doesn't get him his money back but it helps. *(he gets a cap out of his bag, holds up a 10p, shows it to the group, and drops it in)* OK?

40

Pause as the idea sinks in.

TOM	OK. I'm in. *(he rummages in his wallet and pays into the cap)*

| ANDREW | I haven't got any money. | 45 |

TOM   *(rummaging again and dropping in another)* You can owe me.

Gradually all join in, dropping in their money. Nigel stares, his grin widening.

GEMMA   I've only got a 20p. *(drops it in)*

BEN   And that's 10p change. *(hands it over)*

Scene 16

Slowly, the rest of the class join in, forming a queue.

CRAIG   I've only got a quid.

DARREN   I've only got two 50s.

ALISON   OK, Darren, you give him a 50 and me a 50. And … I'll give you two 20s and a 10 … and Neil, you give Darren your quid … and I'll   5 give you … No. Hang on. Start again. *(they hand it all back)* Right, Darren, give Neil your two 50s. Neil, give Darren your pound. *(they swap)* No, hang on, that hasn't got us anywhere, has it? Right, Neil, I swap my two   10 20s and a 10 for one of your 50s. *(they do)* Neil, you give them to Darren, and he gives you the pound. *(they do)* No … hang on …. *(they continue, drifting into the background)*

Scene 17

In a different part of the queue.

LIAM   *(to Robbie)* Your dad's loaded. You should put in 20p.

ROBBIE	How do you know my dad's loaded? Anyway, according to you, your dad gave you a tenner for cleaning his car. Bit generous, isn't he? Maybe you should put in 50p. Or a pound.

5

Scene 18

At the front of the queue.

SARA	*(to Ben, putting in her 10p)* Alright?
BEN	You changed your mind, then. About the money, I mean.
SARA	Yeah well, you were right, you know. It's not fair on Nigel, is it?

5

BEN	No. It's not fair on a lot of people. Me, you, Snotty Tom … everyone looking, thinking it might be us who took the money. If I could get him his tenner back, I would … but, you know, this is … second best.

10

SARA	Nice one.
BEN	Yeah. *(pause)* Right, who's next. Neil?
NEIL	*(putting his money in)* Seems like a good deal for a lesson, really. 10p down, one biscuit up. It's all worked out OK, really, hasn't it?

15

Scene 19

As the queue tails through, on one side of the classroom …

ALISON	Gemma, can I talk to you for a minute?
GEMMA	Yeah, 'course.

ALISON   I'm really worried.

GEMMA   Why?

ALISON   About … about the biscuit thing. 'Cos   5
            someone's going to tell someone, aren't they?
            Someone's going to tell someone and they'll
            find out it was me and Tom and the school's
            bound to tell my mum and … *(shrugs in
            despair)*

            *The queue finally ends. Ben starts counting the
            money.*

GEMMA   Oi! Everyone? Listen. Oi! *(finally the group is*   10
            silent) About the biscuits … you can't tell
            anyone. OK? Because it wasn't Alison and
            Snotty Tom that took those biscuits. It was
            all of us. OK?

LIAM   Eh?   15

GEMMA   It could have been any of us who went to the
            office – we drew straws, remember? It just
            happened it was Alison and Snotty Tom who
            got the short straws. But they did it – and
            they did it for all of us. So if anyone tells, if   20
            Alison and Tom get done for it, we're all
            going to get done. I'll make sure of that. OK?

DAN   So we can't even tell—

GEMMA   You can't tell anyone. No one. Not a word.
            OK?   25

            *Silent agreement from the group. Alison smiles at
            Gemma. Gemma acknowledges Alison with a nod.*

GEMMA   *(aside, as she walks away)* Fat chance …

Scene 20

NEIL	What's the grand total, then, Ben?
BEN	*(counts)* Two pounds … Two pounds ten. Hang on … *(counts heads in classroom)* Hang on, we're 10p short.
NIGEL	I haven't paid. I haven't got any money. 5
BEN	We know that, Nige. We worked it out. There's someone else.

Everyone scans the classroom. All eyes end up on Kayleigh. Eventually, she gives into the pressure.

KAYLEIGH	Oh, for God's sake … *(stamps her way to the front and pays her 10p)*
BEN	*(hands the collection over)* There you go, Nige. Two pounds twenty. 10
NIGEL	*(lost for words)* Thanks, guys. Thanks, everyone. Thanks. Thanks. Thanks. No, really. Thanks.
ROBBIE	Hey, Nigel. Have you looked in your pockets? For your tenner, I mean? 15
NIGEL	Yeah, 'course. *(he rummages in his pockets. His face drops. He pulls out a small, crumpled piece of paper, unfolds it. Silence. The class prepare to groan and shout – but it's a torn piece of A4 paper)* Maths homework. *(smiles, crumples it up again and puts it back in his pocket)*
LIAM	Are you sure you put your money in your pencil case, Nige?
NIGEL	Yeah, 'course. Put it in there this morning. 20
LIAM	Talk us through it, Nigel.

ROBBIE	Yeah, good idea. Tell us exactly what happened this morning. *Exactly* what happened.	
NIGEL	Well … I was in the living room …	25
ROBBIE	What were you doing in there?	
NIGEL	Watching telly.	
LIAM	Time for a reconstruction, I think. *(Liam sits Nigel down. A chair is placed in front of him to be the television)* OK. You on your own?	
NIGEL	No, my little brother's in there. *(Liam grabs Stuart, puts him in a chair next to Nigel. Stuart sucks his thumb. Nigel looks at him)* He's nine! He doesn't suck his thumb!	30
LIAM	What you watching on telly?	
NIGEL	Cartoon.	
ROBBIE	Then what?	35
NIGEL	My Mum calls me …	
LIAM	*(in a high-pitched, 'Mum' voice)* Ni-i-i-i-gel! Sweetie pie! Ni-i-i-i-gel, my little treasure!	
NIGEL	Yeah, something like that.	
LIAM	So you go out and find her in the …	40
NIGEL	Kitchen.	
LIAM	Come on then. I'll be your mum.	

Nigel stands, walks to Liam.

LIAM	What did she want?	
NIGEL	She gave me a tenner. Said it was dinner money for the week. Said she'd kill me if I lost it.	45

Liam mimes looking in a purse, handing money over, wagging a warning finger.

LIAM (*'Mum' voice*) And don't spend it all at once. When I was your age—

ROBBIE And then?

NIGEL I went back to the living room. 50

LIAM Go on then.

NIGEL (*miming as he speaks*) I went back to the living room, put the money in my pencil case, put the pencil case in my bag.

ROBBIE Your brother still there? 55

NIGEL Yeah.

ROBBIE And then?

NIGEL (*pauses to think*) My mum started shouting again …

LIAM (*'Mum' voice*) Ni-i-i-i-gel! 60

NIGEL So I went out to the kitchen again … but she was upstairs. In the bathroom … something about putting towels in the wash … can't remember …

But Liam and Robbie aren't listening. As he speaks, their eyes fall on Nigel's little brother – played by Stuart.

LIAM And your little brother … he's sitting there all along? 65

NIGEL Yeah.

STUART What you staring at me for?

ROBBIE And he's watching while you put a tenner in your pencil case? 70

NIGEL	Yeah.
LIAM	And he's watching while you put your pencil case in your bag?
NIGEL	Yeah.
STUART	Stop staring at me! 75
ROBBIE	And that was the last time you saw the tenner?
NIGEL	*(suddenly he sees)* Ye-e-eah!
ROBBIE	How long were you out of the room?
NIGEL	I dunno. Five minutes?
LIAM	Plenty of time for him to nick it. 80
ROBBIE	How long does it take a nine-year-old to take a ten pound note out of a pencil case?
NIGEL	*(angry)* The little ba—
LIAM	Sorted.
ROBBIE	Sounds a bit like it, doesn't it? 85
NIGEL	I'm gonna – I'm gonna – I'm gonna—
LIAM	You're gonna give us all 10p back tomorrow, that's what you're gonna.

Robbie and Liam sit side by side, hands folded behind heads with the smug satisfaction of detectives having solved a difficult case.

Scene 21

KATIE	Hey, what's the time?
HATTIE	Two minutes to go!
DARREN	Till what?
HATTIE	The end of the lesson, idiot.
DARREN	Can we go early, d'you think? 5

| STUART | 'Course not, you moron. We've got to do it just like there was a teacher here – wait till the bell goes. |

| HATTIE | Hey, d'you think we got away with it? |

| LIAM | Well, dur, there's no one here, is there? 10 |

| GEMMA | Doesn't mean we've got away with it for ever. |

| NEIL | They'll find out. They always find out. |

| LIAM | Oh come on, no one died, no one even got hurt, just a few missing biscuits, they're too busy to care about us doing nothing for an 15 hour … |

| ROBBIE | Doing nothing? Doing nothing? I solved a major theft, thank you very much. |

| LIAM | So did I! You couldn't have done it without me! I might join the police when I'm older. 20 |

| ROBBIE | You might spend a lot of time with the police – but somehow I don't think you'll be the one wearing the uniform … |

Scene 22

| KAYLEIGH | So … was it what you wanted? |

| GEMMA | Eh? |

| KAYLEIGH | The lesson. Was it something to tell the grandchildren about? |

| GEMMA | Dunno. 5 |

| KAYLEIGH | But it was alright, wasn't it? |

| GEMMA | It was good. You know, I've found out stuff I never knew about people … I've talked to people in here I've never even spoken to before. Sat in the same room with them for 10 |

... years and never even spoken to them. I didn't know that girl's name before today. *(nods towards Roni)*

KAYLEIGH   Better than an English lesson, anyway.

GEMMA   Miss Barraclough'll be back tomorrow. Or the day after. They always come back.   15

HATTIE   Ten seconds to go!

ALL   *(gradually joining in)* Ten ... nine ... eight ... seven ... six ... five ... four ... three ... two ... one ...

Silence. One or two check their watches.

LIAM   Hattie, what number is the big hand   20
pointing to?

A buzzer signals the end of the lesson. Cheers. Everyone grabs their bags and leaves in a cheerful, noisy crowd – except Robbie and Liam who remain in their seats, still pleased with their detective work.

Scene 23

LIAM   What we got next, then, Robbie?

ROBBIE   French.

LIAM   So that's it then. Adventure over. Back to normal.

ROBBIE   Yup. *(pause)* Was it worth it, Liam?   5

LIAM   What do you mean, worth it? Worth it if we get caught?

ROBBIE   No, I mean ... Is anything any better than if we hadn't done it? If we'd gone and got a teacher? What's changed?   10

LIAM   Nothing. The clever kids are still clever. The thick kids are still thick. Normal lesson.

ROBBIE   I think I learn something most days.

LIAM   Oh, I learn something most days – but it's not what the teachers want me to learn. 15 The clever kids go to school and come out clever, the thick kids come out thick … maybe a bit less thick. But that's how it is. It's alright for you. You're not rubbish at anything … whatever you do, you're good 20 at it. Try being thick and see how you like school. Try being a failure, every day, all year.

ROBBIE   Fun?

LIAM   No, not much. So I got good at being bad. I'm an expert. I'm getting better at it every 25 day. D'you know how many times school phoned my mum last week? Six. That's once a day. *(counts on fingers)* Twice on one day. How many times did they phone your mum and tell her how good you are? Once? Less? 30 *(smiles, nodding with satisfaction)* Yeaahhhh!

ROBBIE   You're not *that* bad. You were alright that lesson. You helped Nigel out. And you're not threatening to thump me anymore.

LIAM   Oh, I can't be bad without a teacher. If they 35 want me to be bad, they've got to send a teacher to the lesson.

They smile. Robbie leaves. Liam, with one last look round the classroom, leaves, closing the door behind him.

Activities

Activity 1: The play's setting: classrooms and education

This activity asks you to consider the importance of the setting in *Free!*, where most of the action takes place in one classroom, and how the playwright portrays education.

a **In pairs,** discuss the following:
  - What is the purpose of education?
  - What is the difference between an inspiring classroom and a drab one?
  - Agree five things you would expect to find in an inspiring classroom.

b **Individually,** read Act One Scene 1 and consider whether the classroom portrayed is an inspiring or uninspiring one. Write brief notes to support your ideas. Share your ideas in groups or pairs, supporting them with evidence from the text.

c **In your group or pair,** choose six lines of the dialogue in this scene that are high in excitement to interest the audience. Pick six lines of dialogue that convey boredom and routine. Prepare a brief choral performance to represent these two opposing ideas (excitement and boredom) in this scene. Rehearse and perform this to the class.

Activity 2: The play's characters; first impressions and real people

This activity asks you to consider what we learn about character in Scenes 5 and 6 and how this develops what we learn from the cast list.

a Look at the cast list on page vii. Decide which character is the nearest to how you would be regarded in your lessons at school. Can you think of another social situation in your life out of school where other people might think you are very different from this?

b The playwright develops our understanding of the characters in the classroom by showing their different reactions to having no teacher and their opinions about what should be done. Write out the following names below (Gemma, Robbie, Briony, Liam, Neil) and draw a thought bubble above each one. Summarise the thoughts of each of the characters at the end of this scene and write them in each thought bubble.

c **As a class,** prepare a tableaux of the five characters from **b** at the front of the class, thinking carefully about the body language and positioning of each character. Individual students can then come up to the front to stand behind a character and voice their thoughts.

Activity 3: Teachers

This activity asks you to consider how realistic the portrayal of the teachers is in the play or whether it tells us more about the pupils and their reaction to the school system.

a **In pairs,** agree the six top qualities of a good secondary teacher.

b **In groups of four,** skim and scan Act One Scenes 3, 4, and 8 for opinions about teachers. What can you find out about:
   - Miss Barraclough
   - supply teachers
   - Mr Bonnington
   - Mr Smallwood.

   Create a table like the one below and note down your findings with relevant quotations.

Teacher	Findings
Miss Barraclough	
Supply teachers	
Mr Bonnington	

c Share your findings **with the class** and discuss how realistic you think this information is. Are we given two-dimensional (unrealistic) or three-dimensional (realistic) portrayals of teachers in this play? What could the playwright be suggesting about education systems?

Activity 4: Persuasive speech

This activity asks you to think about the features of a persuasive text, and the kind of language Gemma uses to influence her peers in Act One Scene 11.

a Look at the list below and identify which features you would expect to find in a persuasive text:
- direct addresses to the audience using 'you' or 'we'
- vocabulary appropriate to the audience
- references or images familiar to the audience
- counterarguments to dismiss others' points of view
- short sentences for emphasis
- rhetorical questions
- chronological sequences
- imperative verbs
- very little use of imagery or descriptive language
- connectives which indicate sequence.

b Find a quotation in Gemma's dialogue from Act One Scene 11 for each of the features you have selected. Write these out in a table.

c **As a class,** select volunteers to take the place of Gemma in the hot seat at the front of class. Spend five minutes thinking of questions you might want to ask Gemma if you were a member of her class. Then carry out a hot seating activity. The person taking the role of Gemma should try to imitate her powerful way of speaking.

Activity 5: Dramatic tension

This activity asks you to explore the term 'dramatic tension' and its purpose in drama. Act One Scenes 12–17 in the play build tension in the plot as the class and the audience wait to learn which pupils should undertake the challenge.

a **With your partner or a group,** discuss what you think the phrase 'dramatic tension' means. List films or television programmes that you think contain dramatic tension and decide what you think the purpose of this is. You may want to consider the use of this device in soap operas and how it is used at the end of many episodes.

b **Working in pairs,** choose two or three scenes from Scenes 12–17 to reread, thinking carefully about where the audience would feel tense, and where they would feel more relaxed and relieved.

c Identify three points in your chosen scenes that you think reflect the most significant points of tension or relief for the audience. Copy out a quotation for each and write a comment to explain your choice. You could use the sentence starters below:

This is a significant point of tension in Scene x because...
This point in the scene offers a relief from the tension because...

Activity 6: The biscuit tin drama

This activity asks you to focus on the thoughts, feelings and actions of Alison and Tom. Act One Scene 18 reports on the height of the drama in the play and a turning point for Alison and Tom.

a There are two timeframes in this scene; the playwright switches between the previous action in Miss Dixon's office and the pupils' return to the classroom to tell their classmates. **In pairs,** reread the scene and identify the action and dialogue that has happened in Miss Dixon's office. You need to understand how it is different from 'present time' events as Alison and Tom return to the classroom.

b **Working in groups of four or five,** (Tom, Alison, Mrs Dixon, Mr Bonnington plus a director) select and sculpt five still images to represent the action of the biscuit tin drama.

Or

Individually prepare a storyboard of five images that reflect the five significant events in the scene in Miss Dixon's office.

c Add the thoughts and feelings of a couple of characters from each image. For groups doing the drama activity, these can be spoken by the director once agreed by the group. For individuals drawing a storyboard, these can be written as thought bubbles.

Activity 7: Formal language

This activity asks you to write a message from Miss Dixon and think carefully about the kind of formal language and tone that she might use. We learn about Miss Dixon through the comments of pupils. They see her as formal and strict.

a **With a partner,** find the sections of the play that have mentioned Miss Dixon and create a table like the one below to record your conclusions about her personality (see Act One Scene 11 and Act One Scene 18).

Scene	Quote	Conclusion

b Imagine you are Miss Dixon. You have found out that the biscuits in your tin have gone missing and may have come to some conclusions about how that has happened. Write a message to the head of year about the events and your suspicions. Make sure that your language is appropriately formal, and that you refer to specific events in your office from Scene 18. Check that your message has some conclusion of what you would like the head of year to do about the situation.

c Underline what you think are your three best examples of formal phrases or vocabulary in your writing. Share these **with a partner**.

Activity 8: Considering the character of Liam

This activity asks you to consider both sides to Liam's character and find supporting evidence in the text. As the play develops the audience learn more about the character of Liam. He has many positive qualities that are different from his reputation as the 'difficult student'.

a **With a partner,** use a large piece of paper to draw a silhouette of Liam. Alternatively you might like to find a picture in a magazine of a teenager that matches your visual picture of Liam. Leave space on either side to write notes about his character. Draw a vertical line down the paper through the image to divide the page into two. Entitle each column 'virtues' or 'vices'.

b Each of you should choose whether you would like to focus on Liam's virtues (good points) or his vices (bad points). Then skim and scan your text to select five relevant quotations to illustrate different positive or negative points about Liam's character. Write up five points plus quotations on the relevant side of your paper.

c Write a brief character analysis of Liam, using the PEE method (point, evidence, explanation), including comments on both his positive and negative characteristics.

Activity 9: The themes of the play

This activity asks you to focus on the themes of the play and how they are conveyed through the dialogue and actions of the characters. David Grant encourages the audience to consider various themes in relation to the characters and setting of *Free!*

a Look at the list below and **with a partner** agree what you think are the four most important themes in the play.

- education,
- friendship,
- the family,
- discipline,
- achievement,
- struggle,
- self discipline,
- love.

b Read the introduction to the play and consider what the playwright says in relation to the four themes you have chosen. Check that you are happy with your choices.

c Take a piece of A4 paper and divide it into four. Write the title of each of your four themes at the top of each box. **With your partner,** consider a question about each of these four themes that you would like to ask the playwright.

d When you have done this, swap your paper with another pair and see if you can answer their questions as if you were the playwright, using evidence from the play to support your answers. You could also do this activity **as a whole class** with the teacher or a volunteer in the hot seat as David Grant.

Activity 10: Authoring a scene

This activity asks you to consider the character of Nigel and how he might react when he next returns home to his mother and brother.

a **With a partner or group,** discuss what the audience already knows about Nigel's character from Act Two Scene 2 to Act Two Scene 20.

b Look carefully at the final lines of Act Two Scene 20. How does Nigel feel about his brother? What might he have learnt from the reactions of his classmates about his missing money?

c Reread Act Two Scene 20 to remind yourself about Nigel's family and the events leading up to the missing money. Share ideas **with your group** about how Nigel might react when he next sees his mother and his brother. Then plan and write your own extra scene for the play, set in Nigel's home, to follow Act Two Scene 20. Remember to set out your script with speakers' names and stage directions using your play script as a model.

Activity 11: Advertising the production

This activity asks you to plan and author a flier of a production of *Free!* at your school, combining persuasive language and information you have learnt about the play, its characters and themes. Theatre companies produce marketing material to inform and persuade their audiences to visit their productions. Examples of marketing materials are fliers, posters and website information.

a Look at some examples of marketing materials about plays produced in your local area. You will be able find this on the website of your local theatre. Alternatively, look at the website of the Royal Shakespeare Company to see what information is given about current productions. A link to the site can be found at www.heinemann.co.uk/hotlinks by clicking on the link to Free!
  - Write down the facts that need to be included about a play's production.
  - Write down some examples of persuasive language that are used.

b Plan what you would need to include on a flier advertising a production of Free! at your school. Remember to include both factual information and persuasive elements.

c Design and write your own flier for your production.